THE EVOLUTION
OF MAN

BY

WILHELM BÖLSCHE

———

Translated by ERNEST UNTERMANN

———

SEVENTEENTH THOUSAND.

CHICAGO
CHARLES H. KERR & COMPANY
1918

PREFACE

Whoever claims to be an educated man, a man who thinks, must acquire a knowledge of the outline of modern scientific research and of the theories concerning the descent of man. No thought is so essential and sublime as that about ourselves. One may be skeptical as to the value of these things, but before any discussion of them is possible, one must, above all, think.

There must be no class distinction in view of these questions. Wherever great philosophies and movements in their interest have appeared in history, they have not addressed themselves merely to the kings of the spirit, but instinctively to the simple man of the people, to that place where the heart of the people is beating. Since natural science to-day claims to offer a new basis for a scientific world philosophy, it must again address itself to the common people. It may seem that scientific methods of expression and thought are an obstacle to popularization. If so, we must take so much the more pains to overcome this obstacle and find a popular interpretation for our thoughts. The present little volume is addressed to the widest circle of readers, even to those who are as yet unacquainted with a goodly number of excellent but much more voluminous works concerning the same subject. This little work is reduced to such a size that it may easily be perused in one leisure hour. Nevertheless I think that the facts which it presents will furnish material for independent reflection in serious hours.

As for its scientific basis, I have only to mention the name of Darwin. Whoever thinks himself beyond this name in our days is specially invited to analyze his theories once more by the help of this short and comprehensive sketch. In its more intricate details my presentation of the matter is naturally based on certain ideas of Ernst Haeckel, but I must also give due credit to the great influence which the more recent researches of Herman Klaatsch of Heidelberg have exerted upon me. Whenever I have ventured beyond the line of facts, or combination of facts, I have done so from my own firm conviction that a thinking man is not dragged down by all these relations with the animal world, but is

PREFACE

rather strengthened and furthered in the consciousness of his own ethical powers. He then appears to me so much more triumphant above his animal nature, standing victoriously above the dark foundation of his own existence. Man and his history reach back into the primitive world of animal monsters, but this animal nature, this primitive world, lies prostrate at his feet overcome by himself.

WILHELM BOELSCHE.

Friedrichshagen,
New Year's Day, 1904.

THE EVOLUTION OF MAN

A lovely picture extends before my eyes. A virgin meadow stretches down a valley clad in emerald green. Innumerable blossoms of dandelions and blue-bells rise from it like golden and violet flames. A gray granite wall, a witness of primordial days, forms the background to this fresh wave of full life. Above it, like a dark blue stage setting, rise the fir forest and the opposite mountain wall. And far, far beyond it, almost merging into the soft blue sky with a slightly deeper tint, appears the outline of the giant mountains. Now, a snow-white cloud, glistening in the sunlight, floats slowly and phantom-like towards me, coming down from the unknown distance beyond, and disappearing above me in the glittering light. The bright glow of the sun is diffused throughout it all, lending charm to the flowery meadow, the granite and the

9

mountain forest—a great unity sunk in harmonious tranquility. Now, I hear far-off voices. Human beings are passing by, shielded from my sight by the great stone blocks. They are strangers, I do not know them. How much may be hidden by such distant voices—good and bad! What an infinite variety is comprised in this little word "man," how much that is noble and sublime—and how much that is brutal! And yet, while those feeble undulations of the air which carry those voices toward me are still trembling in my ear, I am thinking of the simple message of the gospel, according to which all men without distinction are my brothers. Our civilization has at last risen to the point of impressing us with the fact that this many-headed mass of fifteen hundred million people on the surface of this globe are bound by one common tie of sacredness which is expressed in the word, man! They are all one unit, these human beings, one great family assembled on the surface of this globe, ready to share their sins, to forgive one another, to enjoy their pleasures together, to go hand in hand on their way through this great valley of riddles, the universe.

But a clearer and sharper sound, not articulated into words, mingles with those indistinct voices. It is the fine voice of a little baby, this monotonous and clear wail which sounds so helpless and yet stirs so much compassion!

We all have grown up, we all have developed from such a small baby, such a bud of humanity. And my glance wanders once more over the green meadow. All those golden blossoms of dandelions and all the blue-bells have developed from a bud. Every one of those plants has grown up into the sunlight from some simple germ. And it seems to me that it is this same sun which neither of them can dispense with. The little rosebud of humanity in its cradle needs the sun quite as much as that brown, rough bud of yonder meadow flower. If the sun above us which is floating in the ice-cold solitude of space ninety-six millions miles away were to be extinguished to-day, humanity would perish just as surely as the kingdom of meadow flowers.

And from the depths of the human soul, whence also the lessons of the gospels have come, still another voice whispers into my inner ear. It is that same voice which was first heard in the wisdom of ancient India, and it said that the tie of common interest, of brotherhood, is not confined to man and man, that it comprises all living things of this globe, all things which grow up under the rays of the sun in the silent grasp of secret, natural laws, and gradually develop to the summit of humanity. It is that other simple message which tells us: "Thou shalt not torture any animal uselessly; thou shalt not wantonly break any flower, for they too are distant relations in the great flow of life, they too are still your brothers in the unfathomable recesses of nature. Helpless stands that flower, or that glittering little beetle before you, just like a trembling, little child. But the child grows up into a man, and who knows what this flower or that beetle may become some day, or what may have become of others like them, millions of years ago!

It is such sentiments as these which every one of us feels in his or her best moments which seem to me fitting for the discussion of such a tremendous question as that of the evolution of man.

Wherever the compassion of man can find its way, there the blessed and divine longing for understanding may also wend its steps without fear or shame. Whoever has so much love that he can feel it for an animal may also approach with perfectly clear conscience that other question, whether the blood relationship that freely binds him to other human beings does not perhaps extend still further, whether he himself may not have developed from an animal. And he may recognize with calm conviction that this fact cannot have any more significance morally than that other fact which is affirmed a thousand times every day and sanctified by the deep love of every mother—the fact that even the greatest man must have first developed from a primitive, human bud, from a child which can neither speak nor walk, which germinates in the dark recesses of nature, just as that blue bell out there develops under the hot rays of the sun. And if the individual develops in this way, why should not all humanity have developed in this way, once upon a time?

It was about a million years ago. If a man could have had the opportunity to wander through our present European continent, with a rifle in his hands, he would have seen in those days a very strange country. He might have imagined that he was in the interior of Africa as we know it to-day. He would have tramped for weeks over immense prairies in Southern Europe, dotted sporadically with a few dense woods, and out of the wilderness of this green ocean of grass, he would have started before him innumerable herds of antelopes, giraffes and animals resembling wild horses. From his camp near a rippling spring, he could have watched in the clear moonlight, such colossal forms coming to drink and to bathe as were once seen by the first hunters who ventured into the interior of Africa by way of Cape Colony. There, he could have seen elephants of various species, with two and four tusks, or even with tusks bent downward like those of the walrus, massive rhinoceros, and ponderous hippopotami. Behind them he could have heard the roaring of lions, panthers, and giant wild-cats armed with saber-like teeth. Wandering further north into localities which are now the scenes of a highly advanced civilization, he would have entered the most impenetrable, primeval forest, similar to that in which Stanley in the heart of Africa experienced all the sensations of daring conquest of an absolutely wild tropical country. Out of the dense undergrowth, splendid palms rose toward the sunlight. Parrots of many colors shrieked, the features of a large anthropoid ape, similar to our gorilla, might peep suddenly out of the thick covering of foliage, piercing the daring intruder with sharp glances. And above it all, there trembled the atmosphere of a hot climate.

Our wanderer would have been still more surprised if he could have compared our present-day maps with the road traveled by him in those primeval days. Where the blue surface of the Mediterranean now extends so widely that a navigator cannot see the shores on either side, he would have advanced over dry ground from horizon to horizon through prairies inhabited by giraffes and forests peopled by monkeys. And where to-day the red rose of the Alps grows upon dizzy heights near the grim ice of the glaciers on mountain passes, there he would have found nothing but wooded hills in which his geologically trained eye might have discovered traces of a slow but irresistible rise. And where to-day the sun is sending its glowing rays down upon bare mountain ranges, as in the heart of France, he could have observed the horizon tinted blood-red, a reflection of the boiling lava of volcanoes.

A strange world in an immeasurably far off time!

A million years is a tremendous period of time for human minds to grasp. If the history of human civilization is traced by written chronicles, it does not take us back beyond six thousand years. One might fill entire libraries with events through which human beings have passed merely in a period of one thousand years. Here, we are supposed to place side by side thousands of thousands of years. What wonder then if the mirror of research transports us back to those primeval times into a different Europe, composed of different seas, countries, mountains and climates.

It is the so called "Tertiary Period" into which we have looked.

Four great periods are distinguished by the historians of the earth, in speaking of the change and succession of animal and plant life as it is discovered in the course of the many million years during which it has developed. We may use the simple Latin numbers to designate these periods: Primus, the First, Secundus, the Second, Tertius, the Third, Quartus, the Fourth. There is the Primary period, the very first in which we discover traces of living beings on our earth. It was then that the forests were green, the fossil remains of which we now know as coal. Strange and uncouth newts crawled about in their shade. The sea, the shores of which were covered by these trees, was alive with long forgotten crustaceans and fishes. Then followed the Secondary period, in which the terrible giant saurians, typified by Ichthyosaurus, infested land and sea. After that we reach the third great period, the Tertiary period, when Europe had the climate and the fauna of present day Africa, such as giraffes, elephants and monkeys. And when this epoch came to an end, the Quaternary period began, with which our entire historical tradition is identified and in which we are stll living to-day. We do not meet any familiar objects until we reach this last period. The surface of the earth then assumes the form to which we are now accustomed. All things come closer to us. The things that lie beyond are strange to us, like an unknown creation, like a dream of some other planet.

And yet man lived even in that Tertiary period. No song, no heroic story, gives any information about him. But where the voice of tradition, the chronicles of conscious humanity are silent, there we find other witnesses that speak to us—the stones. The tradition of mankind expires within the Quaternary period. There is an extreme moment when even the most ancient inscriptions of the Chinese, the Babylonians, and the Egyptians become mute. Written characters disappear and with them the earliest direct voice from the cradle of humanity about itself. But beyond that point we are made aware of a very important event in the development of this earth which took place in this Quaternary period, the traces of which are still visibly impressed in the rocks. It is the great ice age. For many thousand years, colossal masses of glacial ice were piled on top of the continents of Europe and North America. Large herds of mammoth, a species of elephant, covered with a thick coating of hair as a protection against the cold, grazed along the edge of these glaciers, just as in our day the musk-ox and the reindeer are doing in the countries near the North Pole. Undeniable and plain traces of human beings are still preserved from that period.

In the sand, which remained when the glaciers flowed into the caves which were formed by the mighty ice waters boring their way through the lime rocks, the crude and simple stone tools have been found with which the men of that period hunted the mammoth. The walls of such caves in France are still covered with colored pictures in which the men of that ice age have drawn unmistakable pictures of the mammoth. As it happens we are enabled to test the accuracy of those pictures, since well preserved bodies of mammoth with skin and hair are found in the ice of Siberia. We have also found the skulls and bones of those men, so that we now have a fairly good idea of their characteristics, in spite of the fact that all written and oral traditions of the civilized nations now living have completely forgotten their ancestors of the ice age. Even the most sublime symbolical picture of the evolution of civilization, the Bible, does not mention them anywhere.

But those simple stone tools, especially knives and arrowheads, which give us such reliable information of man as the contemporary of the mammoth, are occasionally found also in the strata of rock which were already present when the ice age with its glaciers and mammoths began. We find in them remains of that most primitive human civilization, together with bones of a giant elephant, who was not only larger and of different form than the mammoth, but also older—the so-called South-elephant (Elephas meridionalis.) But this South-elephant was still living in laurel groves and under magnolia blossoms in France and Germany, instead of feeding on reindeer lichens on the edges of the glaciers. With this elephant we have come into the middle of the genuine Tertiary period. This Tertiary period, the more we follow it backwards, takes us into a warmer climate instead of a colder one. In the middle of this period we meet with that very picture which I drew in the beginning. Europe then had the giraffe plains and the primeval forests of the present day inhabited by anthropoid apes, and there is no longer any doubt that the oldest tools of man, which we can distinguish as such, lead us even to the limit of this very hot, middle period of the Tertiary age. Man is even then a part of that picture! He is himself almost a million years old on the surface of this globe, and had simple stone weapons and other tools which he used in his fight with the giant animals of that time. In other words, he possessed the indubitable beginnings of civilization.

It seems to me that we cannot trace matters up to this point without confronting this further question: Is it not possible that man may be still older?

With this venerable age of one million years he is a part of the wonders of the primitive world, he drifts into the company of still stranger animals than the mammoth, into other climates than those of present-day Europe, the Alps of which were then in the first stage of formation and the seas of which had not yet found their present level. So it really would not change matters very much even if we found that we must trace him further back into still more ancient and strange landscapes of this globe. It is true that all traces of civilization disappear at this point. We do not know of a single piece of flint stone in the first half of the Tertiary period, or even of the saurian period following it, which would show the traces of the human hand. But long before we reach this point, we may observe a gradual divergence of these flint stone tools. They grow cruder and cruder. Is it too wild a speculation to suppose that men may have existed even beyond that time who may not have possessed sufficient civilization even to fashion the simplest stone tools? In that case, we could not expect to find any stone tools as witnesses.

But, one might say, there should at least be genuine human bones preserved in a fossil state in the solid rocks together with skeletons of the ichthyosaurians? Still, this objection would not carry much weight. We know very well that not all of the living beings which once lived upon this earth left their fossil bones behind. The bones may have been destroyed, for human bones particularly are not very durable. Or they may be buried in certain places of the earth which we cannot investigate to-day, because they may be at the bottom of the sea, or covered by the perennial ice of polar regions. How often has not this earth been shaken through and through and turned inside out in these long, long periods? Strata, which were once sediment at the bottom of the sea and which are still full of sea shells, are now found on the high summits of the Alps. On the other hand, entire mountain ranges, ground into sand, are now found in the flat sandstone of the plains, or at the bottom of the sea. Many of the remains of the primitive world have certainly been destroyed in this wild chaos, have been ground into powder, or broken to pieces. We get a vague conception of this when we see that even the gigantic monsters of those primitive days have frequently left but one single bone, a thigh bone or skull of one single individual. That is to say, while thousands and thousands of individuals of this species lived once upon a time, only the scant remains of one single individual have come down to our time.

Then too, there is still another possibility which is far more interesting. It is very probable that we may not recognize the man of those far distant days, even if some of his bones were preserved. For man himself might have become transformed in his structure, and his bones might differ from ours. Might it not be possible that his bones might look so strange to us that scientists might have described them as belonging to some other being, little aware of the fact that these remains represented just the thing for which they were looking?

Similar ideas have ever played a role in various tales and legends. There, we read that the men of the primitive world were gnomes, or again giants, Cyclopes with one eye, or fauns with goat's feet, tails and pointed ears. When mammoth bones were first found, it was said that they were the actual remains of such old fabulous men, bones of the giants Gog and Magog, or of St. Christopher. Of course, this was nonsense, and the supposed human bones were nothing but honest mammoth bones with no relation to primitive man. But, we of to-day have really something better than mere remains to rely on, we have reliable scientific data for the theory that men with essentially different characteristics from ours existed not so very long ago.

I mentioned, a while ago, that we have remains of skeletons of men who lived in the ice age, the age of mammoths. But these men of the

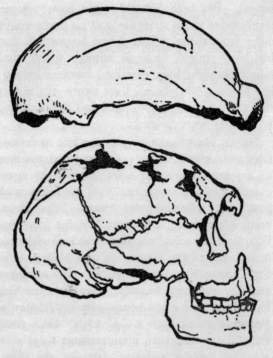

Two remains of skulls of *palaeo-diluvian Men,* with strongly protruding eye-bumps. Both cuts are side views. The cut at the top represents the skull-cap (the only part which was preserved) found in 1856 in a cave of the Neander valley near Düsseldorf, Germany. The cut at the bottom represents a fairly complete skull, found in 1887 in a cave of Spy, near Namur, France, together with equally aged bones of *Mammoths, Rhinoceros,* and *Cave-Bears.*

ice age, who are still relatively close to us when compared to the more distant primitive periods, are not so very much behind in their civilization when compared to certain savage peoples of to-day. Even in our day, there are certain tribes, for instance in South America, who are not familiar with metals, who fashion all their tools and weapons out of stone, horn, or wood, and who therefore are actually living in the "Stone Age" similar to those primitive mammoth hunters. Nevertheless, if one of us had met one of these primtive ice age men, we should have been somewhat startled by the features of that man. For his face, his size and his limbs would have appeared to us perceptibly different from ours, even from those of the savages of the present day. True, no one would have doubted that this was still a "man," but something strange, something divergent, would certainly have startled us in this type of the "Ice-age man." We may still reconstruct this man tolerably well from the remains of his skeleton.

It was in 1856 that such genuine human bones, with strangely divergent characteristics, were discovered for the first time and scientifically analyzed. It was in the so-called Neander Valley near Dusseldorf (Rhineland). Some working men were clearing out an old cave. They found an old and partly decayed skeleton. A physician, Dr. Fuhlrott, happened along and saved as many of these bones as he could obtain. In this way they reached a museum, and they are now on exhibition in the Provincial Museum of Bonn. The student is especially surprised by the construction of the skull of this man, which is very flat in the part directly above the brain, and has thick and unsightly bumps right over the cavities of the eyes. Even the lowest Australian has no such bumps on his forehead to-day.

For a long time the genuineness of this discovery was doubted, and no correct conclusions could be formed because the experts could not agree on the period to which this Neander Valley skull should be assigned. Some even doubted whether this man was really very old and whether he could have been a contemporary of the mammoth. Rudolph Virchow then took part in the discussion and claimed that whatever might be the antiquity of these bones, and granting that they might be genuine bones of a contemporary of the mammoth, they certainly did not belong to a normal man, but rather to one who was diseased. The divergence from the present human type was attributed to the effects of disease. It

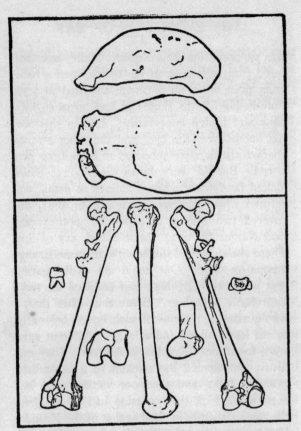

REMAINS OF PITHECANTHROPUS ERECTUS,

the mysterious being found by Eugene Dubois on the island of Java. The cut shows a skull-cap, seen from the side and from the top, with its bumps above the eyes; furthermore several views of the left thigh-bone, and two molar teeth. The thigh-bone has on its inner side some abnormal formations due, probably, to some wound which this specimen received while alive.

was supposed that this Neander Valley man suffered from softening of the bones when a baby, from gout when an old man, and that at some time in his life his skull had been crushed by a blow and healed imperfectly. And in this way the bumps over the eyes and the other strange characteristics were supposed to have been produced. But this very daring assumption, which looked far-fetched when examined in detail, was refuted when Professor Fraipont, in 1887, discovered two human skeletons in another cave near Namur (France), the so-called cave of Spy. These skeletons had skulls with the same strange bumps on them. One could not easily assume that all these individuals had endured the same improbable sufferings. Some time after that, a whole mass of remains of such bones, belonging to not less than ten individuals of different ages, were found near Krapina in Austria. They evidently represented the remains of a prehistoric cannibal feast, and the poor victims who had been roasted on that occasion had all of them the same structure of skull as that of the Neander Valley man. And, finally Schwalbe and Klaatsch have demonstrated scientifically that the Neander Valley bones were not at all diseased.

It is quite certain, then, that a type of man

with such skulls has once existed, and the discoveries at Spy and Krapina have shown at the same time to what period that man belonged. They were found together with the bones of the mammoth and cave bear of exactly the same age. They were therefore remains of "Ice-age" men, and these ice-age men still showed this strange divergence from the present living type of "man."

Now, let us imagine that these variations continued far into the more primitive period. The traces of civilization, as we have seen, finally disappear altogether. Man himself, if present in those very primitive periods, would not have been advanced far enough to fashion the crudest weapons out of flint stone. And we may logically draw conclusions from this lack of ability as to his physical constitution. The man of the Ice-age was able to fashion weapons from flint-stones, and yet he was far behind us in the structure of his skull. How far behind, then, in the structure of his skull, would be a man without knowledge of flint stone tools?

The line of research here absolutely dissolves into nothing. Man diverges more and more from the present type of human beings. He finally varies to an extent which makes him absolutely indistinguishable and hides "Man" in beings which are not at all like him.

We must recall to mind the millions of years of the primitive world, the infinite succession of time, and think on and on along this line of natural development, just as we would in the case of a star which, once started on a defintie course from a certain point, continues to move and move incessantly in a certain fixed direction.

But now that we have gone so far, we feel a pardonable curiosity and a certain daring. Would it not be possible for our penetration, once we have conceived of these possibilities, to forge ahead still farther into the mystery of things, get at the facts of all these "possibilities," and ask what disguise man might have adopted? What may be those strange primitive beings, the fossil remains of which we might perhaps find and in which he may be most likely hidden?

We have at least a starting point. We perceive, so to say, the mathematical point where the course begins to deviate, that is to say, we may start from these grotesque skulls of the ice-age with their crude bumps above the eyes. May we not speculate a little further as to the next physical transformation, and so forth?

THE EVOLUTION OF MAN

It is precisely at this point that we meet with something which has the great advantage of not being merely a logical assumption, but rather a tangible scientific fact.

The beautiful island of Java in the tropics has long been known on account of its violent volcanic eruptions. As late as the Tertiary period there was an eruption of a certain volcano which buried an entire section of land with loose masses of ashes in the same way in which Mt. Vesuvius buried the city of Pompeii in historical times. On this occasion a multitude of living beings were buried. Their bones remained in that volcanic mass and were later on carried to a certain place by waters washing their way through this mass. The name of this place to-day is Trinil, and the old mass of volcanic ashes is now a part of the bed of the Bengavan river. In 1891 a Dutch physician, Eugen Dubois, made excavations in the banks of this river, and incidentally he discovered masses of old bones, mostly the bones of large mammals of the Tertiary period, such as elephants and hippopotami which do not live in Java in our day. But among those bones Dubois found also a thigh bone and skull cap and a pair of molar teeth of a peculiar creature which had evidently lived in those primitive days with those animals at the time when the eruption of that volcano occurred.

This creature must have had a strange likeness to human beings. It had almost the height of a man. Its upper thigh indicates that it had the habit of walking upright. Indeed, it was so manlike that a number of authorities in anatomy, for instance Rudolph Virchow, declared without hesitation that it was a genuine human bone. But matters were different with the skull. Flat, without a forehead, and with bumps above his eyes, this skull seemed in its fundamental plan to be an extreme exaggeration of the Neander Valley skull. But this exaggeration went so far that the human likeness receded against a new likeness. This Trinil skull resembled strikingly —a monkey skull. And it was even possible to name the definite species of monkey which it resembled most nearly, a monkey living to this day in Southern Asia, the so-called gibbon. The gibbon is the nearest relative of the ourangoutang, the gorilla and the chimpanzee. The present living species are all of them much smaller than this strange creature of Trinil was. But that old skull was, in many respects, so like that of the gibbon that quite a number of grave experts declared that it belonged to an extinct species of gibbon which had the size of a man.

Still, a few others did not agree with this idea. The cavity of the skull, so far as it was preserved, was filled with gypsum in order to find out how much space it contained for a brain. The figure ascertained by this means was approximately half-way between a gorilla and the lowest Australian aborigine. That is to say, its brain capacity exceeded by far that of a gibbon without however coming anywhere near that of present-day man or even the ice-age man. What sort of a creature could this be? The scientists disagreed. "A very gibbon-like man," said some of them. "A very man-like gibbon," said the others. The discoverer Dubois took a middle course; he baptized this creature with the double name of Pithecanthropus, monkey-man.

This disagreement of the scientists is very instructive in our research. We learn, as an actual fact, that in the Tertiary period there still existed on this globe certain creatures which stood about half-way between a man and a gibbon. Their skull exaggerated those characteristics, by which the ice-age man was distinguished from present-day man, to such an extent that this creature approached a new station which we have long known by the name of monkeys. In this way we are given a definite goal indicating the first disguise in which we may look for man further back and discover him, so to say, by evidences which reveal his presence beyond that limit where he began to deviate entirely from the present type of man.

Is it perhaps possible that at a certain historical stage man simply merges in the monkey? Here another very old and venerable line of reasoning, long used even in the most exact research of nature, comes to our aid.

It was in 1735 that Linnaeus, a great scientist, performed a monumental work. He then gave us the first comprehensive system of nature's forms. He arranged these forms in three great kingdoms, minerals, plants, animals. And within these kingdoms he arranged the various forms in systematic succession. In this way, he furnished us with a system of plants, and of animals, which, in spite of its defects, gave us the first foundation for a comparative view and logical sequence by which we could hope to discover the natural connections of these forms in their main outlines.

In performing this necessary work of genius, Linnaeus naturally had to solve the question: Where am I to place man? He did not hesitate for one moment. He placed man in the animal kingdom on account of his physical structure, which showed that he belonged to the mammals, and more definitely in the group of monkeys. Indeed, if we wish to build up any system even in our day, that is the only logical conclusion at which we can arrive. Man is not a simple mineral, he is a living being. Unless he is fed, he dies; that is to say, his form of existence is that of living beings who are compelled on pain of death to assimilate food. If we pinch his arm, he cries out; in other words, he feels, and he has that peculiar faculty which we are accustomed to associate with the word "life," the faculty of subjective feeling. Furthermore his food is of a definite kind. He cannot feed on pure mineral substances, he requires either vegetable or animal matter, he needs bread instead of stones, and of the elements of the air he can utilize only oxygen. This classes him with the other members of the animal kingdom in distinction from plants which feed on the soil.

Again, in the animal kingdom there are two main groups. It is true that Linnaeus himself was not familiar with this distinction, but we have learned it since then. The individual body of the animal in one of these groups consists of only one so-called cell. It is one solitary little lump of animated substance. The individual body in the other group of animals is composed of many such cells, which form a sort of co-operative association with division of labor. Well then, the body of man is built up with billions of such cells in the most wonderful manner. It consists of living building material, the cells, which make up its muscles, its blood, its skin and even its bones. In other words, man belongs to the group of animals that contain many cells. He does not belong to the uni-cellular low arch-types, he is not a microscopically small infusorium.

This higher group of animals is again divided into a number of groups, among which we must make our choice. There are the sponges, the polypi, the jelly-fish, the worms, the star-fish, the echinoderms, the crustaceans, the insects, the snails, the shells, and, finally, a group which is distinguished by a spinal cord located above the digestive tract and protected by a more or less solid structure which serves at the same time for the support of the body, a backbone. We call this last group the vertebrates. No other group has this characteristic structure, and it is plain, at the first glance, that man can belong only to this group, because he has a spinal cord

AN OLD ORANG-OUTANG.
His face is disfigured by peculiar excrescences on both cheeks.

and a backbone. Within this group of vertebrates we distinguish the fish, which breathe in the water with gills instead of lungs; man breathes through lungs, therefore he is not a fish. Then follow the amphibians, that is to say, the newts and frogs that breathe alternately through gills and lungs. A frog, for instance, breathes through gills, when a tadpole, and acquires his lungs later on. Human beings do not have this double method of breathing. Furthermore, the reptiles, that is to say, lizards, crocodiles, turtles and related animals have blood which changes its temperature from warm to cold and vice versa. Their blood is cold when the air which they breathe is cold, but it is warm when the sun shines upon them. These animals do not yet possess their own heating apparatus within them. The human body heats itself, it is always warm, hence man is not a reptile. The two last groups of vertebrates are always warm. These groups consist of birds and mammals. Since we have to choose between these two, we must investigate further. No bird suckles its young, but the human mother does that, and all mammals do, therefore we belong on the side of the mammals. Now these mammals are again divided into two great sections. Those of one section lay eggs, the Australian duckbills. The mammals of the other section have done away with that; the child when born is far more mature. Every human mother testifies to the fact that human beings are not duckbills, but belong to a higher class. And now we come to a final choice. We look at the hands and teeth of man. Man is not a whale, the hands of which have turned into fins. He is not a carnivorous animal which has one-sidedly developed its eye-teeth and incisors. He is not an animal with hoofs which has laid special stress upon its molar teeth. He is not a rodent, the best trumps of which are the incisors; he is not a sloth, the teeth of which have entirely degenerated, nor is he a bat, the hands of which are made into wings. There is only one single group of mammals, the teeth and hands of which resemble those of man, and that group is composed of monkeys.

Mark well: when Linnaeus placed man side by side with the monkeys in his system, he was not thinking of anything else but just an orderly arrangement, a systematic grouping of animals at a greater or smaller distance, just as a boy will stick his beetles into his collection, some closer, others farther apart. But since the days of Linnaeus a good many deep thinkers and clear heads have asked the question whether this "system" might not have a deeper meaning and relation to nature?

Now, when we remember that we arrived at a certain station in our research which we named monkey-man, the probability of a deeper meaning of that system grows apace. We were looking for some primitive disguise by which man might have concealed his identity far back in the days of the primitive world, and we must certainly say, when we think of this system, that of all the creatures of this globe, none is better fitted for such a disguise than is the monkey, that is to say, that animal which in spite of all the differences of its bony structure is still far more like us than all the other living beings of the earth together.

Remember also that we were not speaking of monkeys in a general way; but indicated a certain species, the gibbon. Systematic zoology very early accomplished the separation of some species of monkeys from others, the so-called anthropoid apes. This word indicates that these apes are still closer to man in the system than any others. No other group in the system is so close to us. We now distinguish four species of these anthorpoid apes. Two of them are living in Africa, the gorilla and the chimpanzee, and two in Asia, the orang-outang and the gibbon. These four apes strangely resemble human beings, even externally. The layman is specially astonished to notice that they, like man, have not an externally visible tail. But scientists know that this occurs occasionally even among lower monkeys and so it is not considered a very convincing mark. But there is a very wonderful relation which should convince the most inveterate skeptic, and that is the following.

Whoever has looked at a drop of blood through a very strong microscope knows that this peculiar fluid is a mixture of two things, first, the so-called serum, and then the blood corpuscles floating round in it. Now when we compare the drops of blood of various animal species, we find that the red blood corpuscles have many different forms. Some of them are long, some are round, some are large and some small; in brief they are different in fish, or newt, or bird, or mammal. This is no ground for surprise, for all these animals are very different in many other ways.

The peculiar significance of this difference is that the attempt to inoculate an animal of one group with the living blood of another group always ends fatally. It is just as if these two kinds of blood carried on a war with one another. The serum of one group destroys the blood corpuscles of another group. If an animal is inoculated with the blood of another group, it quickly feels the fatal effects of this struggle in its veins. It falls into convulsions and finally collapses entirely, just as a conflagration consumes a city in whose streets a violent civil war is raging. And this happens often in the case of animals which are relatively close to one another, for instance, many mammals. The blood of a cat kills a rabbit which is inoculated with it, and vice versa. But finally there is a certain limit. The blood of a cat naturally does not kill another cat. Indeed, peace is guaranteed often among more distant relatives. Closely related animals may mix their blood without danger. A dog is so close to a wolf that the living blood of the one may mix with that of the other without harm. It is the same with a horse and a donkey. Now a short time ago a certain scientist, Friedenthal in Berlin, mixed human blood and monkey blood. At first one blood acted as a poison for the other; that is to say, as long as the objects of the experiment were man and a lower monkey. But when human blood came to the blood of the chimpanzee, peace was suddenly established. The boundary of antagonisms had been crossed. The blood of man and that of the anthropoid ape were so nearly akin that they agreed without difficutly. How could this be? Here it was not a question of comparing bone with bone. An answer came directly from the living. The secret of life, the most minute chemistry of the blood, testified to the most intimate relationship, a consanguinity in the most daring sense of the word.

With this fact we have made another step ahead. The probability grows that man may have been concealed once upon a time in one of these creatures which we see represented by the anthropoid apes of to-day. Indeed ,the experiment with blood makes it almost evident that all four anthropoid apes now living are directly connected with this mysterious primeval fact. The question is only, what is this relation?

We first of all feel tempted to ask whether these anthropoid apes themselves might not represent that primitive stage for which we are looking. Are not these apes veritable primitive men that have not yet been transformed into genuine men to this day?

One thinks involuntarily of the ludicrous tales of the negroes who say that the gorilla and the chimpanzee are really men, only they are too lazy to work, and for this reason pretend that they are monkeys. And perhaps there is sufficient truth in this theory to justify the belief that these apes actually represent a type of primitive man who was arrested in his development against his will, and who went so far in his conservatism that he still illustrates the "monkey stage" of man.

Again one might ask at this point, how it is that a few of our crude and monkey-like great-grandfathers are still living in the form of isolated men of the woods, as a fixed primitive type, at a time when present-day genuine man has long arrived at his perfect form. But we meet with the same phenomenon within genuine humanity itself. Why does the native Australian with his Stone Age civilization still live in the bush, while over here civilized man has already risen to the full height of his evolution? And we have an illustration still closer at hand. In the plains where the modern metropolis steams and roars, progress walks with seven-leagued boots, while yonder in the remote mountain village ancient customs and institutions are still in full bloom. So, this would not be a very pertinent objection.

However, let us take a closer look at the anthropoid apes. We have four species. These four species differ considerably from one another, some of them show even extreme differences. Do they possibly represent four different primitive stages of man? But every attempt to reconstruct them from a continuously ascending line towards man is a complete failure. It is true that each species has a number of its own peculiar resemblances to man. But, it rather seems that these resemblances are distributed among them in a rather indiscriminate way, so that they all supplement one another in a fundamental outline of man, but nevertheless do not form an ascending chain of evidence.

We now remember that strange creature of Trinil, and our attention turns especially to the gibbon. Is it possible that he could be a genuine archetype, and that the orang-outang, the chimpanzee and the gorilla could be merely unprogressive branches? One thing cannot be denied: this gibbon possesses indeed very strange and portentous characteristics. It seems that this ape actually brings us closer to the secret of our descent. He is not a bestial gorilla, but a much more gentle and soulful creature. He can sing the music of the scale,—a very strange case in a mammal, which involuntarily reminds us that it is precisely in man that language and song

A GIBBON.

The anthropoid apes of the gibbon group are living in southern Asia and in the Sunda Islands. They have extremely long arms, which are much longer than their legs. The gibbon has very significant relations with the human line of descent.

have developed. Furthermore, if the gibbon descends from a tree to the ground which, by the way, he does not like to do, he walks habitually on two legs and balances himself at the same time by stretching out his arms sideways, or folding them above his head, and these arms of the present-day gibbon are again a new clue in our research. Compared to the trunk and the legs these arms are excessively long. Any comparison with man seems impossible in view of these arms. No other mammal has arms of such length. However, if we study the habits of gibbon life, we easily recognize their purpose. The gibbon is the cleverest climber among the anthropoid apes. He is an unexcelled acrobat, thanks to these arms. They represent an extreme but very adequate adaptation to his special needs. But when it comes to comparing him with modern man, these arms of the gibbon certainly point away from us. The question arises whether the primitive man for whom we are looking could ever have had such spiderlike arms. The gorilla, chimpanzee and ourang-outang also have pretty long arms, but they are not nearly so long, and in that respect these apes seem to be much closer to man. Even a majority of the lower apes, such as Macacus. and even the baboons, have a much closer resemblance to man in this one point.

There seems to be only one way out of these strange contradictions. We must conclude that the living anthropoid apes are closely related to the archetype of man for which we are looking, but they do not represent its thorough-bred type. Each one of them has developed along his own line from this thorough-bred type simultaneously with man as we know him to-day. They did not change very much, but still they went far enough to acquire each his own peculiarities. All of them retain strong resemblances to the archetype, but one has preserved more of some characteristics and lost others, while the reverse is true of another species. Very likely the gibbon still resembles that archetype most closely, but even he has later acquired those enormous arms.

It is highly interesting to know that we may mention a direct reason for our general assumption of probability, so that it becomes almost a certainty. Among living beings there is a very curious law, or at least a near approach to one. Young animals very frequently resemble the ancestors of their whole race more nearly than the adult animals. A frog in the tadpole stage still resembles a fish which breathes in the water through gills. A great number of higher animals assume again in the egg, or in the mother's womb, certain forms which we meet on a much lower and more ancient plane. A bird in the egg shows for a while a great mass of vertebrae, in its tail which once characterized the extinct bird-lizard (Archaopteryx), a transition form between lizard and bird, existing millions of years ago. Haeckel has called this peculiar fact, which recurs in innumerable cases and truly indicates a general and lawful connection, the "biogenetic principle," and this term has become fairly popular to-day.

Well, then, the very first observers noticed that the gorilla, the chimpanzee, the orang-outang, resemble man more in proportion as they are younger. The giant gorilla, which is the most ferocious and bestial of all anthropoid apes in old age, resembles in its baby stage the human being so closely that even the layman who has never thought about these things is surprised. In view of the biogenetic law, this would indicate that these anthropoid apes are descended from an ancestor who was still more manlike than they are to-day. And the point is finally clinched by some facts which the scientist, Emil Selenka, has recently discovered in regard to the gibbon. An unborn gibbon in its mother's womb at first has well proportioned arms just as if it were to become a human being. And it is only by gradual stages that the arms of the little ape develop into those enormous acrobatic limbs. If the biogenetic law is correct, then we would have in this case an exact proof that the ancestors of the present-day gibbon did not possess those long arms and were, therefore, considerably more manlike.

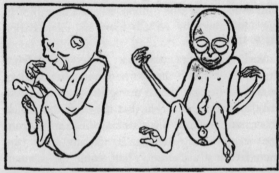

EMBRYOS OF A GIBBON,

in an advanced state of development. Mark the likeness to a human embryo.

(After Selenka.)

Thousands of indications thus point to the fact which occurred even to Darwin when he discussed these things tentatively for the first time, some thirty years ago. A species of mammal has once existed on this globe which contained the germs, not alone of man, but also of the gorilla, the chimpanzee, the orang-outang and the gibbon. All of them have later developed from that type—unlike sons of the same father. No doubt this creature was, in some respects, a closer copy of the present anthropoid apes than of modern man, and it must have been closest to the gibbon of to-day. However, it was distinguished from this gibbon, as we know him in his adult form by certain more manlike marks. And if we were to call that primitive being "man," because genuine man is descended from him and because he has such strong resemblances to human beings, then we might say of the present-day anthropoid apes that they are descended from man, instead of man being descended from the orang-outang, or the gorilla, as some laymen frequently claim. That would be a much more correct statement, and would conform to the idea of Darwin, who gave rise to these discussions.

That primitive type is no longer living on this globe. Unless an unexpected discovery is made in the partly unexplored forest regions of the interior of Africa, we may close the books in this matter. At this point then, our steps must be directed exclusively towards the primitive world. But, what can be said in regard to those primitive bones and the possibility of fitting them into the picture which we have just drawn?

Here we remember once more that famous Pithecanthropus of Trinil, who is half gibbon, half man. Is it possible that he could be the very type for which we are looking? There is one thing which gives rise to doubts, and that is the time to which he belongs. We have seen that it is almost a certainty that genuine man lived in the second third of the Tertiary period, that is to say, in those tropical forests of middle Europe. Recently, flintstone tools have been found in France in the strata of that period, which the scientist called the "Miocene Period." These tools are almost identical with certain stone tools of the crudest kind which every expert attributes to human hands. But the great forests of this Miocene period were inhabited by man-like apes. In Austria, Switzerland and France, there lived a genuine gibbon (Pliopithecus) and another species lived in France, closely resembling the chimpanzee, but yet standing by itself without being any closer to man (Dryopithecus). A little later we also find genuine chimpanzees and orang-outangs. So much we can tell by well preserved bones. It is evident that the unlike sons of that mysterious archetype had already branched off at that period, and the types had become so plain that they could be separated into anthropoid apes and men.

It seems, however, that the bones of Pithecanthropus, which we know belonged to the extreme end of the Tertiary period, are apparently many thousand years younger than those bones of the Miocene period. If that creature of Trinil still contained in the germ a common thoroughbred type, then it follows that this type must have lived simultaneously with its unlike sons on the island of Java, even after the lapse of so many thousand years.

Of course, such a thing would not be impossible. Only we might ask whether that thoroughbred type could have been preserved in its original form during this entire period. We might be inclined to suspect at least some of the least typical characteristics and assume that this type might have developed a little further and adapted itself to the new conditions, while nevertheless it might still give us a far better idea of the actual course of development than the present anthropoid apes.

THE EVOLUTION OF MAN

It is also logical to ask whether Pithecanthropus was not a long surviving "last Mohican" of a transition form from a genuine thoroughbred type to the genuine man. It all depends upon the weight which we lay upon the specifically genuine human marks. If any one is more attracted by the resemblance of that form to the present gibbon, he might argue that Pithecanthropus was a transition form from the archetype of past genuine man to the genuine gibbon. This last theory might be seriously considered from the moment that we could get a glimpse of the arms of that archetype, which we do not know as yet, provided they were to show a tendency toward the grotesque elongation of the genuine gibbon arm. Let us hope that the excavations in Java will be diligently pursued and that we may then be able to solve some of these more intricate problems.

So much at least is certain, that the genuine common ancestor in question, who must have had at least a very close resemblance to Pithecanthropus in the structure of his skull and legs, existed before the Miocene period, that is to say, in the first third of the Tertiary period. He represented the "Man" of that time—a creature which contained the possibilities of development into genuine man and also those of development into a gibbon, chimpanzee, gorilla and orang-outang. Doubtless the greater part of his body was covered with strong hair, such as the present anthropoid apes have inherited from him. He is a real, genuine, living "Esau." The fact that the smooth "Jacob," man of to-day, has only a very slight indication of this hairy covering on most parts of his body, is not a proof to the contrary. For we find the instructive law on the resemblances of the youthful forms to their ancestors gives us a very satisfactory clue to our original ancestor: the body of the human being in the mother's womb is also, in its first stages, covered with thick woolly hair. Even the face is covered just as we see it to-day in the case of the adult gibbon, and only the inner surfaces of the hands and feet are left free. Evidently these free places were uncovered, even in the ancestor which this human embryo copies for a short time. This Esau-like covering of the human being does not disappear until immediately before birth, and in a few exceptional cases, this covering has even been retained during life. This is the origin of the renowned men with dog faces.

Now we come to a new question. What is the ancestor of that archetype? In what other disguise can we trace him further back? In the system, the four anthropoid apes are followed by the rest of the monkeys. This class again consists of at least three great groups which differ from one another. Some of them are the long-tailed monkeys of Asia and Africa, such as Macacus, baboons, etc., which make up the majority of the popular monkeys in our zoological gardens. The second group lives exclusively in America, and the bright Capuchin monkey may be mentioned as a type. The third, also restricted to America, comprises a small number of little monkeys, having claws instead of nails on most of their fingers and toes and resembling much more a squirrel than a genuine monkey. The marmoset is one of them. These three groups can no more be used in the construction of a consecutive line of development than the four anthropoid apes. But a purely anatomical comparison leaves the impression that somewhere near them the next lower stage of man must be found.

Even the very first experts who described the gibbon noticed that this same gibbon, aside from his strong resemblances to the other anthropoid apes and to man himself, also had certain other resemblances very plainly developed, and these pointed towards the Macacus-like long-tailed monkeys. These characters could be inherited only from the archetype, and this type again could only have inherited them from some still older type, which had a general and much greater resemblance to the majority of the other monkeys. That there was once upon a time a certain ancestor who had an externally visible long tail is still evidenced by man himself. Not only is man in the tailed stage to this day, though the tail vertebrae are no longer externally visible, but these are certainly still better developed in man than in the anthropoid apes. Furthermore, the human embryo in the mother's womb once more reveals the persistency of that mysterious biogenetic law. It has a plainly, visible external tail. In exceptional cases this "embryo tail" is also preserved in adults, and in some cases we have those abnormal "tail men," whose existence has often been doubted, but who nevertheless exist. There is no reason why we should not assume that certain Macacus-like types, preceding the human type, carried a genuine tail for a constant characteristic. So far as we can judge from fossil remains of bones, genuine long-tailed monkeys, similar to those in present Asia, were already in existence in the middle of the Tertiary period, in which both man and anthropoid apes were found. One species, Mesopithecus, lived in great numbers in Greece, where many bones of them have been found. This Grecian monkey had a very long tail. At the same time the form of its nose and the position of its eyes gave it a greater resemblance to the human being than any of the present long-tailed monkeys have. On the other hand, the light hearted crowd of long-tailed monkeys has developed many characteristics which tend toward a direction leading away from man. There are, so to say, one-sidedly bestialized forms, an extreme exaggeration of which is the baboon family, for instance, the grotesque mandril. The conclusion is inevitable that once again, at this point, a line of descent originally close to man has gradually deviated into a bypath and produced many varieties of monkeys now living in Asia and Africa. Therefore we should once more have to assume the existence of an archetype out of which developed, on the one hand, the original ancestor of man and of the anthropoid apes, and, on the other, that Grecian Mesopithecus and the many side lines of African and Asian long-tailed monkeys. Of course, this archetype would have to be still a great deal more ancient than the preceding one. It might have existed as early as the first third of the Tertiary period. By its external characteristics, we should certainly have classed it among the genuine monkeys, and only a few slight anatomical marks would have betrayed to the expert that he was not dealing with a monkey of later descent, but with one in which, so to say, the third generation of coming man was still concealed.

Now, it is peculiar that we have actually found remains of monkey-like animals in the first third of the Tertiary period. They were discovered by the Spanish explorer Ameghino in Patagonia, the extreme end of South America, and were concealed in a layer of rock which must have been developed toward the end of that first third of the Tertiary period. We call this first third the "Eocene" period, or in English the dawn of the more recent period. When Ameghino first analyzed one of these Patagonian monkey skulls, it conjured up to his imagination the ghost of a very small man, so that he called it "Homunculus," but it seems that after all this resemblance to man is not much greater than that of the American monkeys of the Capuchin type, and that group of Eocene monkeys evidently belonged to that class. It cannot be denied that the present Capuchin monkey is in many respects, physically and mentally, man-like. It also has secret relations with the gibbon, and thus to the archetype of the Pithecanthropus kind. Thus, many things favor the more recent assumption that possibly these bright, gentle and highly intelligent American Capuchin monkeys are the closest of any of the present monkey forms to that genuine monkey type of man which belongs to the Eocene period.

On the other hand, the small and squirrel-like marmosets must be eliminated from our line of descent and regarded as a side line. Most likely they are a one-sided adaptation to special conditions in South America.

But now that we have gotten so far, there can be no doubt as to the next question. If man can be traced so far back in monkeydom, he cannot but share all the vicissitudes of monkey life further back. Whatever may be the general descent of monkeys, that is at the same time the line of man's development. The prototype of monkeys is also that of man.

The conventional system of mammals proceeds along a great downward scale. First we have the prosimiae, bats, insectivora, such as the hedge-hog, then carnivora, rodents, the large and

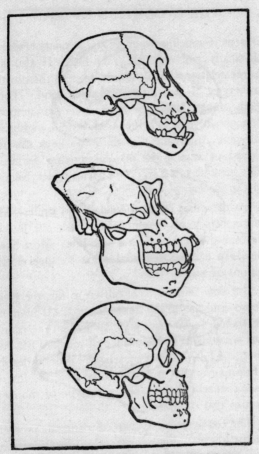

THREE SKULLS FOR COMPARISON.

The skull at the top is that of a *young Gorilla*, the one in the middle that of an *old Gorilla*, the one at the bottom that of a *Man*. Note how much more man-like the skull of the young gorilla is than that of the old one.

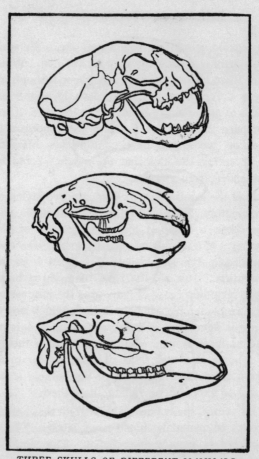

THREE SKULLS OF DIFFERENT MAMMALS.

At the top is the skull of a carnivore, a *Cat;* in the middle that of a rodent, a *Hare;* and at the bottom that of an ungulate, a *Horse.*

variegated group of ruminants, etc. But this scale is only apparently a historical one. Whoever were to imagine that man went through all these different stages in succession would not come to any definite result. For instance, if we compare the teeth of a rabbit with those of a monkey, we should have considerable difficulty in accepting the idea that the monkey could be descended from a rabbit.

It is the same when we compare two styles of architecture. The one is simple and noble and the other a sort of bizarre caricature of the former. We do not take kindly to the idea that the simple style should have developed from the caricature. Just so, the rows of teeth of monkeys, including those of man, give the impression of a simple temple of noble style, in which everything is developed in conformity with a definite and uniform system. But the teeth of a rabbit, of a horse, and even those of a cat, appear to us like a caricatured variation of that simple style, going to excess here, falling short there.

Of course, the opposite idea that all these other groups of mammals should have developed from monkeys is equally improbable. The simplest historical premises oppose such an idea. Neither do the remains of bones of primitive animals teach us that there were at a certain period, first, let us say, ruminants, later on, perhaps rodents, then carnivora, and finally monkeys. Nor do they show that there were at first no other higher mammals than monkeys, and then in successive periods ruminants, rodents, etc. We rather receive the impression that all of these groups appeared simultaneously at a certain period.

Now it is precisely the progress in our knowledge of extinct mammals which succeeded finally in leading us out of this labyrinth of contradictory assumptions.

All those groups of mammals still appeared in the first third of the Tertiary period, the so-called Eocene period, to which we have repeatedly referred. Monkeys, as we have seen, were among them. Hence, if we desire to learn more about the origin of these things, we must trace our steps further back, say to the beginning of this Eocene period.

Now we have found in two places far distant from one another—in France near Cernays in the vicinity of Reims, and in North America in New Mexico—the bones of certain extremely old mammals belonging to just this period, and these bones explain the mystery very fully. On the **one** hand, all of these bones have a very simple and fundamental structure. They show a re-markable row of teeth without extremes, or caricatured exaggerations, and the present monkey and human teeth are easily derived from them. Furthermore, these skeletons have four **feet, or** rather four hands, with five regular fingers, among them one very flexible thumb. This is another very good prototype of the monkey and human hand, which is so widely different from the claw of the lion, or from the shin and hoof of the horse. In place of nails, these five fingers had an indefinite sort of thing, half way between a claw and a hoof, which might easily have developed into anything, say, a horse's hoof, a carnivore's claw, or the nail of a Simian, or a human hand.

On the other side, these animals show the beginnings of certain divergences in the structure of their bones. Some of them have more of the rodent, others more of the carnivore, others of some dominating ruminant character. There is no doubt that these simultaneously represented a very ancient group of ancestors which was just then beginning to branch out into the various great side lines of mammals. And it is equally certain that one of these side lines was composed of monkeys. Of course this original side line of monkeys must have resembled the original ancestor in the structure of teeth and hands and must have been a straight continuation of its evolution in the best sense of the word. This explains why man and monkey, who to this day possess the simple normal teeth and the primitive hand, give the impression, now that the ancient group of ancestors has long become extinct, that carnivore, ruminants, etc., are nothing but very extreme caricatures of the archetype.

Furthermore, the claim that the monkeys were really a side line of that very primitive ancestor, and the most direct side line at that, is substantiated by a study of those ancient bones of Cernays and New Mexico. Just as we still observe in those bones certain variations in the direction of carnivora, of rodents, of ruminants, so we also find a little group of animals which gradually, but very decidedly, move in the direction of our monkeys.

True, they are not yet genuine monkeys, but they certainly show an unmistakable resemblance to a certain group of mammals which have always followed in the system directly after the monkeys, and which were often considered as some peculiar retinue of genuine monkeys, the so-called prosimiae.

TARSIUS SPECTRUM.

This little lemur almost resembles a tree-toad and is related to the family-tree of man.

To this day there is living in the Sunda Islands, that is to say, in the same locality where the gibbon and the orang are living, and where once upon a time Pithecanthropus struggled through his existence, a queer little creature, partly resembling a small **monkey**, partly a leap-mouse, with long stilted legs. This little creature is so funny in all its aspects that it has been called the "tree toad" among mammals. The official name of this little forest gnome is Tarsius spectrum. This Tarsius is counted among the prosimiae in the system. Quite a number of animals about the size of a cat belong to this group, some of them coming from Madagascar, and known as "Makis." Furthermore, there are the so-called Galagos and the very strange Finger-monkey. At a certain period there existed in Madagascar even some species of prosimiae, which were nearly as large as a man.

Now this little Tarsius has a certain character which connects him very closely with the genuine monkeys, first of all with the American Capuchin monkey. Those who have been present at the birth of a human being will remember a certain bloody mass which is forthcoming after the birth of the child. This is the so-called placenta. So long as the little human being rests in its mother's

THE EVOLUTION OF MAN

womb as an embryo, this placenta is its most
important organ, because by its help, the nourishing juices from the blood of the mother pass into
the body of the child and thus feed it. The
various groups of mammals differ considerably in
the method of forming this placenta in the
mother's womb. Man and the anthropoid apes
have their own peculiar method. This is another
excellent proof of the close relationship between
man and these apes, and it was a great acquirement for this science when Selenka demonstrated
that these processes followed the same outline in
the gibbon and the orang-outang as in man—a
process which is otherwise found nowhere but in
man. The Macacus-like, long-tailed monkeys
follow a different method, and the American
monkeys have another and more primitive one.
Now, it is interesting to know that the prosimia
Tarsius follows the model of the American monkeys in forming this placenta, while the majority
of the genuine prosimiae again go their own
peculiar way. And since we have found in
America very old bones of the species Tarsius,
the probability grows that prosimiae of the
Tarsius type may be the direct ancestors of the
American monkeys. If so, it is at the same time
the next station in the evolution of man. This

type of Tarsius of the Tertiary period would certainly represent a further development of our old friends of Cernays and New Mexico, which show certain divergences from the original type in the direction of the prosimia. The scientific name of these prosimiae is Lemuridae, and these very ancient ancestors indicating this direction have therefore been called "Pachylemuridae."

Let us remark in passing that there is still a very little group of mammals, the so-called insectivora, such as the hedge-hog, moles, etc., that likewise have a placenta similar to that of Tarsius. It is among the hedge-hogs that this placenta is distinctly visible. The student can hardly fail to suppose that the hedge-hogs are likewise in some way closely related to the side line which branches off from the archetype in the direction of monkeys. However, this question is not yet settled. At any rate, the hedge-hogs give the impression of being members of a very ancient group, and they, more than any other living mammals of the present day, seem to have preserved most nearly, even in their external structure, the actual form of that primeval group of Cernays and New Mexico.

But, if we try to solve the question of the ancestors of that original group itself, we are brought face to face with another historical fact.

We have now arrived at the beginning of the Tertiary period. One step further back and we find ourselves in the age of the great saurians. The geological picture has now completely changed. We enter the Secondary period of the earth's history, that inconceivably long epoch in which the chalk cliffs of the Island of Rugen, the jurassic slate of Suabia, and the reddish sandstone used in building the Strasburg Munster were formed. The greater part of the large fossil bones belonging to these days were the remains of giant reptiles, some of them resembling dragons. Those saurians swam around in the ocean like our present day whales, or they rolled around in the mud like our hippopotami. Some of them, resembling colossal kangaroos, grazed on the prairies like cows, lumbered about on their heavy hind legs, or jumped after their prey, and some of the most daring even rocked themselves on batlike wings high up in the air. It was not until gradually in the course of this geological period, which probably lasted many millions of years, that birds appeared for the first time—first of all, the lizard-bird Archaeopteryx. This transition form shows very plainly in its structure that birds are merely a side line of the great main branch of reptiles.

Nevertheless, during this typical saurian age, there already existed some mammals, as is proved by the remains of their bones. True, they do not seem to have played a very prominent role. Their remains have been found, therefore, only in a few portions of the secondary strata. And all these scant remains belong to rather small animals, but such as they are they are well preserved and teach us an important lesson.

In our transition from the Tertiary period backward into more primitive times, we become aware of the fact that all higher mammals gradually disappear, even that archetype of Cernays and New Mexico. Instead of them, the remains of mammal bones, wherever they may appear, belong to representatives of a certain group of lower mammals, the so-called marsupials.

The best known type of marsupial is the kangaroo. But there are still a number of other representatives living, most of them in Australia, some of them also in America. These marsupials have, among other peculiarities, a bony projection in their lower jaw, and this always distinguishes their jaw from that of any other mammal. The fossil lower jaws of these secondary mammals always have this very characteristic projection. They evidently belonged to a group of mammals whose last living representatives are the present-day marsupials. These bones are also found in Africa, Asia and Europe, proving that this race of marsupials formerly inhabited the entire earth.

Under these conditions the assumption was justified that this primitive group of mammals represented the most ancient type, from which the tertiary archetype of the higher side lines might have developed. In that case, they once more show us another mile stone in the upward march of disguised man—a marsupial man as a contemporary of the Ichthyosaurian. This general conclusion is confirmed by a good many details.

Marsupials owe their name to a fact, which every child notices in the kangaroos of our zoological gardens, that is to say, the female carries its young, which is born in an immature state, for a while in a protecting fold of its skin, the so-called pocket. In this pocket the young finds the milk-nipples which it uses in suckling as mammals do. To this day, the embryo of the highest mammals, including that of man, bears in the position and surroundings of its milk-nipples certain indications which perceptibly point toward their original location in a pocket, a sure sign that the ancestors of all of them once went through the marsupial stage. A very good proof is furnished by the present living marsupials in their peculiar formation of that important organ of propagation in the mother's womb, which we mentioned once before, the placenta. While in our previous remarks we mentioned only the different forms of this placenta, we now notice that the marsupials seem to have remained stationary at the point where the placenta was in its first stage of development.

The majority of the marsupials have no placenta at all, and this is an indication of a former and still more ancient condition which is closely connected with the existence of a pocket and the premature birth of the young. The young was born so early and required the use of the milk-nipples so prematurely that it did not at all need a placenta connected with the nourishing juices of its mother's blood. On the other hand, a few species of Australian marsupials, the Perameles, show the beginning of a very simple and rudimentary placenta, and thus furnish an additional proof that this important organ went through its first stages in the ranks of the marsupials. In other words, the marsupials represent the genuine ancient transition form from a lower to a higher mammal. We shall have to

A SPECIES OF PERAMELES,

a type of lower marsupials, which, however, forms a sort of placenta and thus approaches the higher mammals.

assume that the progress from these marsupials with primitive placentas toward that archetype of Cernays and New Mexico took place during the chalk period, that is to say, the last great

division of the Secondary age. It is important
to note at the same time that a hand with five
fingers and a flexible thumb, which have been so
faithfully preserved by prosimiae, monkeys, anthropoid apes and man, are found among the
climbing species of marsupials, especially the
American oppossum.

Before the external nipples of the breast are
formed in the human embryo, the milk gland is
formed in the skin. If we remember the biogenetic law, it seems to us that the milk gland
existed in our ancestors at a certain stage before the genuine nipple of the breasts came into
existence. At the same time we see the human
embryo at a certain early stage of its development
with a very peculiar construction of its posterior
opening. The opening for the products of the
urinary and sexual organs is found in the rectum,
so that there is only one single opening for all
three things, the products of the digestive, the
urinary, and the sex organs. It is not until the
third month that a partition is formed in the
rectum of the growing human being by means
of which henceforth these excretions are divided
and discharged through two openings, one for the
products of the urinary and sex organs, the other
for the products of digestion. This succession of

organs compels us to consider whether we have not to deal in this case with a very old inter-relation of things. Could it be possible that mammals concealing man existed once upon a time which possessed milk glands, but no external nipples, and which had only one single opening for the products of the urinary, sex and digestive organs?

There are such mammals even in our day. They are known as Australian duckbills. One species of them, living on dry land, called Echidna, resembles a large hedge-hog and is protected by strong quills. It lives in Australia, Tasmania and New Guinea. Another kind, living in the water and called Ornithorhynchus, resembles in its pelt and habits the otter. It swims very well and lives in the little rivers and lakes of the Australian continent. Both duckbills are without external nipples, but they have genuine milk glands. The milk percolates through a sieve-like place in the skin into the mouth of the young. At the same time the body of the duckbill has only one single opening for the products of the urinary, sex and digestive organs.

In the system these duckbills follow after the marsupials. Neither of them has any placenta. Nor do they need it, and that for a very good

ECHIDNA HYSTRIX,

the land duck-bill, an archetype of mammal living in Australia, which lays eggs like reptiles and birds, but suckles its young after they have hatched. Its egg, natural size, is shown to the right.

reason. They actually lay eggs in the regular way. The young is born in an egg with a parchment-like wall, just like a young turtle or lizard. But while it is hatched from this egg like a young bird, it licks up the milk of its mother mammal fashion. The terrestrial duckbill has furthermore the method of marsupials; it carries first its egg and then its young in its pocket. The aquatic duckbill, on the other hand, does not use this method any more; it digs a hole in the bank of a river, makes a regular nest and there lays its eggs openly, just like a bird.

The inevitable conclusion from these premises

ORNITHORHYNCHUS PARADOXUS,
the water duck-bill, a mammal of Australia which lays eggs and is closely related to the primeval ancestors of present-day mammals.

is that these duckbills show us the more ancient group of ancestors below the marsupials. In other words, Australia has preserved for us a few "last Mohicans," witnesses to a certain stage in the development of mammals and of man in the far off days of the primitive world. And all that would now be required to complete the proof would be genuine historical testimony given by primitive fossil duckbill bones, such as furnished the required proof in the case of the marsupials. For a while it seemed as if this group would not be forthcoming. It is true that various little teeth and remains of small mammal bones, not belonging to any class represented by living mammals, not even the marsupials, were found in the strata of the age of the great saurians far into this first third of the so-called Trias period. Most of the discoveries consisted of teeth, but neither of the two duckbills now living has any teeth. They are called duckbills because their toothless jaws are covered with a horny skin giving them the shape of bird's bills. The aquatic species especially has a genuine duck bill.

However, one fine day the biogenetic law once more came to our rescue. A young duckbill develops in its first stages a sort of milk teeth, having the early characteristics of molar teeth. No teeth of any other living or extinct animal correspond to the form of these teeth of the young duckbill—with the sole exception of those fossil teeth of the saurian age. Hence we conclude that the toothless bills of the duckbills, in spite of the fact that they look so queer in a mammal, do not represent an ancient heritage. They are rather a newly acquired character, an adaptation, which these surviving Australians have acquired during the long period that has elapsed since then. Their ancestors in the saurian age, who were at the same time the genuine ancestors of the higher mammals, had teeth, and these are the very teeth which we now find in a fossil state. These ancient duckbills with teeth, as one might call them, if this term were not self-contradictory, are known by the scientific name of Allotheria.

When duckbills first became known, their bills were, of course, the first thing that gave rise to comment. Owing to their presence these mammals, which otherwise had all the marks of a mammal, gave a decided impression of a cross with birds. For this reason some people speculated from the beginning whether these queer creatures did not actually represent the transition of a mammal to a bird. In the light of the explanation given just now, we are not very much impressed with this speculation, for the bill appears as something unessential and subsequently acquired, which has about the same significance as the whalebone in the jaws of the whale, or the exaggerated claws of the sloth. But the other characteristics of these duckbills concern us much more. There is above all the habit of laying eggs, which had not been ascertained by the first observers. This habit indeed indicates the descent of mammals from a lower class of vertebrates. But this lower class need not necessarily be birds, for reptiles, amphibians and fish also lay eggs. Indeed, the egg of a duckbill resembles much more that of a reptile, such as a lizard, or a turtle, than that of a bird. And if we consider the structure of the skeleton, the resemblance to reptiles exceeds that to birds. The duckbill, the contemporary of saurians, seems to lead directly to the saurians, without touching the birds.

The straight succession of our system misleads us in this instance. Birds represent a subsequent and one-sided branch line of reptiles, and have evidently nothing at all to do with the development of mammals. It is true that the birds have also permanently warm blood like mammals, and owing to this similarity they have been placed side by side in the system. A bird has often warmer blood than a mammal. But this again is one of those qualities which, though indicating a higher stage, were nevertheless acquired independently in widely different periods. In this connection we might point to the fact that the representatives of other dissimilar groups of animals have acquired the faculty of flying independently and at far distant stages. This is the case, for instance, with flies, bees, dragon-flies, butterflies, flying-fish, frogs, such as the flying frog of the Sunda Islands which flies by means of a skin between its separate toes, and lizards, such as the Australian flying lizard. There are, furthermore, the birds, and among mammals, the bats and the flying squirrels. There can be no question whatever of any comparison between the one or the other of these groups in the matter of the flying apparatus. Each one of them, under pressure of conditions, has separately acquired this adaptation. A number of the old and extinct saurians, such as the Dinosaurians, the Pterodaktyls, or flying dragons, must have been in possession of permanently warm blood, so far as we are able to ascertain. A few snakes, such as the python, develop to this day warm blood, under certain conditions, for instance, when they have laid eggs and wish to give them a certain amount of heat in hatching. So, it was natural that the bird should acquire for life a certain faculty which appearel already among reptiles from which it is descended. As we have seen, the strange Archaeopteryx still represents an unmistakable transition form from the general reptile type to the bird. On the other hand, no visible line leads from birds to mammals. The bat is no more such a transition stage than a whale is a transition from mammals to fish. In both cases relatively highly developed mammals have acquired independent adaptations, the bats a flying apparatus and the whales a swimming apparatus.

It is not difficult to imagine that the feathers

of the bird developed out of the scale of the lizard. But it seems quite improbable that either a scale or a feather should have been transformed to such an extent as to assume the characteristic form of hairy covering typical of mammals. Scales, as well as feathers, have evidently been from the very beginning essential means of protecting the skin, either in defense against enemies, or in the case of birds, against the inclemencies of the weather. We observe that scales serve that purpose occasionally even in mammals, for instance, among armadillos. Some whales likewise possessed something like that in former times. But the typical covering of the skin of mammals consists of hair. And it seems that originally hair had nothing to do with protection such as is afforded by scales or feathers, but rather served a wider purpose, embracing not only protection but essentially feeling. The first hair consisted of very fine feelers and performed the functions of touch for the skin. It was not until later on, when mammals acquired warm blood, that hair assumed also the role of a nonconductor of heat.

Now when we look about us to find the beginnings of sense organs of the skin which might have developed into hair, for instance, among lower vertebrates than mammals, we are carried even beyond the scaly reptiles into the ranks of amphibians with naked skins.

In distinction from reptiles, such as lizards, snakes, crocodiles and turtles, the amphibians embrace newts, toads and frogs. While these animals do not have any hair, they nevertheless have peculiar little sense organs precisely in those places of the skin which, among mammals, carry hair and which correspond pretty closely in their arrangement to the plan of the hairy covering of embryos among mammals. According to the biogenetic law, this might very well indicate that the amphibians still show to-day the primitive form of a genuine hairy covering. We might well conclude from this fact that the most ancient mammals, for instance, those creatures belonging to the duckbill family which we discover in the first third of the saurian period, the so-called Trias, are not descended from genuine reptiles, but rather from amphibians which occupy a still lower position in the system.

Now, it happens that the living representatives of amphibians still possess many a detail which might be regarded as an indication of the direct descent of mammals from them. It is remarkable that many frogs and toads have very significant habits of primitive care for their offspring. Sometimes it is the males, sometimes the females, that carry the eggs round with them. The male of the European "Obstetric Toad" has the habit of taking the spawn from the female, wrapping it in strings round its hind legs and taking great care to protect it. The female of the Pipa of South America, on the other hand, carries its eggs on its back, having little pockets in the skin of its back in which the eggs gradually mature and in which the young hatch. Among other toads, the skin has developed large hatching pockets in which first the eggs and later the young animals are carried about in just the same way that we observe among the land duckbills and the marsupials. Furthermore, various glands of the skin play an important role among amphibians. Everyone is acquainted with those glands of the toad which excrete a sharp juice serving as a protection against enemies. But such glands as those play a role in the formation of the pockets of the Pipa. It is not a very far-fetched idea that the young animal hiding in such a pocket might also begin to lick the excretions of its glands, which need not necessarily be caustic, but may serve as nutrition. If that is so, we should find ourselves at once at that stage which is represented among mammals by the duckbill, the young of which licks, during its stay in the pocket, the percolating juice of a gland.

On the other hand, it cannot be denied that the general construction of a duckbill has many

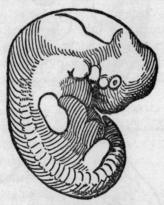

A HUMAN EMBRYO,

in the middle of the fifth week of its development. It is strongly magnified, its natural size being about one centimeter. Note the gill-opening on the neck, the fin-like limbs, and the plainly developed tail.

points resembling those of saurians, in other words, of reptiles. The only marked difference in their skeleton is the way in which the lower jaw is attached to the skull. This separates reptiles and mammals very distinctly. Indeed, the

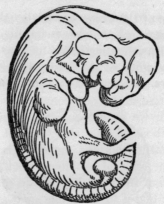

EMBRYO OF A LAND DUCK-BILL.
Note the similarity to the embryos of man and monkey, **both** of them in the same stage of development.

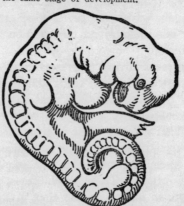

EMBRYO OF A MONKEY
in about the same stage as the human embryo. Note the **similarity** between them.

attachment of the lower jaw to the skull in reptiles and mammals represents the two extremes of two independent methods.

Now the study of the fossils of the primitive world gives us some clue toward a solution of these contradictory questions. The historical time which we should expect to represent the transformation of the most ancient duckbill-like mammals from the archetype next below them in the scale of evolution, would be about the transition from the Primary to the Secondary period, that is to say, a time midway between the carboniferous and the first great saurian epoch. As it happens, it is precisely this time which again gives us some fossil testimony touching unmistakably on the question now under discussion.

The present living representatives of amphibians, such as newts, toads and frogs, were evidently not in existence at that early period. They are apparently a late bud on the branch of amphibian descent. But in their place there existed very strange and large amphibians, some of them resembling crocodiles with more or less solid bony armor. These amphibians possessed many reptilian marks, so that they give the impression that they were in transition from amphibians to reptiles.

Simultaneously with them, there lived certain reptiles, small saurians which in many important respects looked like amphibians and on their part represented a mixed group, the other end of the bridge, so to say. Thanks to a happy coincidence a living grandchild of these amphibian reptiles of the primitive world is still found at this day in New Zealand. Its name is Hatteria punctata. Its entire construction is such that it represents a splendid illustration of the transition form combining the newt and the present-day lizard in an almost neutral shape.

Finally, as a third count, we mention the fact that genuine large reptiles, some of them very grotesque in form, lived in those primitive days. The strange thing about them is that they have undeniable resemblances, especially in the structure of their teeth to mammals. These are the so-called Theromorphoi. Their bones have been found mainly in South Africa, in Cape Colony. Their resemblance to mammals was so striking that their first discoverers naturally thought they had found typical transition forms from reptiles to mammals, and there are still many experts who share this view. Nevertheless, the genuine reptile marks, for instance, the adjustment of the lower jaw, typical of the saurians, are so unde-

niable that there are strong objections to an en-
dorsement of that view. It is not credible that
the reptilian type should have been so well de-

HATTERIA PUNCTATA,
a reptile living in New Zealand, which is a surviving type of
the oldest primeval saurians.

veloped by evolution in the first place and then
continued on towards the mammal type.

If we weigh all the facts, it appears most
probable that a mixed group of ancestors existed

in those days of the latter part of the Primary period, but that this group combined in the germ amphibians, reptiles and mammals, just as we saw at a later stage that the oldest mammals of the Tertiary period took their departure from a mixed group which contained the possibility of evolution into Carnivora, ruminants, rodents and prosimiae.

The members of this mixed group may have resembled the present-day amphibian newts, so far as the naked skin full of glands and sense organs was concerned, and they may have had points of contact with them also as regards their mode of living and otherwise. Their lower jaw may have been so constructed that it might develop in the style of a genuine reptile as well as the other extreme of the genuine mammal, and the remainder of its bony structure may for many ages have resembled the living Hatteria, while other characteristics may have recalled the duckbill. Surely, their feet had five regular toes, one of them probably being a flexible thumb, in other words, the basis of the later "hand." The teeth of this group must have pointed in the direction of mammals.

This mixed group branched off into the various side lines which we have already observed, each one of them laying special emphasis on certain points of the old form, showing the naked newt in one place and the more reptile-like extinct armored amphibian in another, and a genuine reptile in still another place. The reptilians may at first have assumed such forms as we still observe in Hatteria, and out of genuine reptiles developed the birds at a much later period. Still another side line would be represented by those Theromorphoi of Cape Colony which, on the whole, had a pronounced reptilian character, but still preserved in their teeth and in a few other points, such marks as have become typical later on only for mammals. Finally, running parallel with all the others the genuine mammals would have gone their own way.

There is nothing of any consequence to prevent us from assuming that these mammals, which reached their highest stage in man, formed the central line or the crown of the entire line of descent. At any rate, they were the most intelligent line, and they may also have been the most favored physically and have deviated less from the characteristics of the great archetype. In view of all the facts known in this case, these conclusions seem certainly logical and sound.

It is true that genuine fossil remains of this

hypothetical mixed group have not yet been located. But it must be remembered that our discussion is now dealing with sections of the earth's history which are extending into eons of time in which all things are becoming indistinct and vague. To the extent that we venture into the dim past, our proofs must be founded more and more on circumstantial evidence. No one could expect that all the typical stages and their inter-relations should be distinctly seen, it must be sufficient to trace in its approximate outlines the logical course of the main growth. There are a great number of special witnesses to make a good case for our further investigation.

We have now gotten far beyond the saurian period into the so-called Primary age. We are approaching those most ancient epochs which gives us any direct evidence of primitive life on earth by means of petrified specimens. We meet in that period numerous masses of mineral strata, which were once precipitated to the bottom of the sea in the form of mud. These strata bear no other fossil remains of animals than those of fishes. Evidently these were then the sole representatives of the animal world.

We receive the impression that all animal life at that remote Primary age was concentrated in

fishes, amphibians, reptiles and all other vertebrates being contained in fish and no other vertebrate existing beside them.

This historical testimony happens to coincide
exactly with the conventional system in which
the fish follow immediately after the reptiles and
amphibians. A fish is distinguished from an
adult newt, frog, lizard, turtle, bird or mammal,
including man, by the way in which it breathes.
All other vertebrates breathe through lungs in
the open air. But fish represent a perfect adaptation to life in the water. Since a fish, however,
also requires air for breathing, it has developed
an organ which, being continuously surrounded
by water, can assimilate the air contained in this
water. This organ consists of the so-called gills
located in the neck of the fish.

Now, it is a fact well known to every school
boy that the so-called tadpole hatches out of the
eggs of newts, frogs and toads. This tadpole
lives exclusively in the water exactly like a fish,
and breathes only through regular gills. Not until the newt or frog abandons the early stage of
the larva, does it acquire the faculty of breathing through genuine lungs and shed the gills,
much in the same way that human children shed
their milk teeth. The tadpole is nothing less

than an embryo set free. And from the biogenetic law, which recognizes in the embryo the
portrait of its ancestor, we conclude therefore
that newts and frogs are descended from creatures which breathed through gills, that is to say,
descended from fish, since they are the only
vertebrates from which we may choose.

But if these newts and frogs, according to the
assumption that we made a while ago, are nothing but a side line of that main group from
which mammals also developed once upon a
time, nothing remains for us but to assume that
this main group in its entirety leads back to a
preceding station of water animals breathing
through gills.

Some one may object and ask how it is that
no other animals besides frogs and newts, say,
for instance, reptiles, birds and mammals up to
man, have preserved breathing through gills in
the embryonic stage. Why does not a young
human being first become a tadpole before it becomes a man? Well, in the first place, the biogenetic law is not absolute. Very often it shows
itself only in dim outlines. On account of subsequent adaptation for purposes of protection, or
for other reasons, some of those reversions to
type have been subsequently eliminated. The

most useful character in the last analysis prevailed. And wherever a repetition of the characteristics of ancestors was too tedious, this or that stage was finally restricted or entirely eliminated. What good could an early tadpole stage in the water do a bird or a mammal? On the contrary. We see often among certain frogs and newts a tendency to transfer the tadpole stage into the egg, or to go through it before the young is hatched at all. There is, for instance, a tree toad on the Island of Martinique which has become known through such a simplification of the evolutionary process. The tadpole of this little toad no longer hatches out of the egg.

But granted that all this is so, should not the embryo of mammals, reptiles and birds show at least traces of a tadpole or fish stage in the mother's womb, or in the egg? It is the most remarkable proof of the reliability of the biogenetic law that this is actually the case.

No matter what embryo we may study, whether it is that of a lizard, a snake, a crocodile or that of the New Zealand Hatteria, or of a turtle, an ostrich, a stork, a chicken, a canary, a duckbill, a marsupial, a whale, a rabbit, a horse, or finally of a long-tailed American monkey or anthropoid gibbon—the embryo at a certain stage of its development always shows a perceptible tadpole or fish stage. Its neck shows the marks of the gills and the characteristic intervals between them by which the fish breathing in water permits it to circulate freely and flow around the breathing surfaces of the gills. Furthermore, the limbs which the embryos are just forming at this stage have likewise the plain outlines of fins. They push outward in the shape of round disks, and it is only the subsequent development which results in their further transformation, that is to say, into actual fins here, into the swift lower leg of a horse with a single toe there, or finally into the wings of a bird or the flying hand of a bat. If any strict scientific proof were still needed for our claim that all these higher vertebrates converge into a common archetype, it is obviously given everywhere by this common heritage of a gill and fin embryo, either in the egg or in the mother's womb. The gills and fins show that the oldest archetype, with which we are now dealing, was represented by a gill and fin animal—in other words, by a fish.

There still remains this question to be answered: How is it with human beings in this respect? Every text-book on anatomy to-day gives a satisfactory answer. The embryo of human beings at a certain stage is likewise provided with traces of gills on its neck and with finlike disks in the places where arms and legs develop later on. This is as universally accepted as the fact first stated by Copernicus that the earth revolves around the sun. No man who has the least respect for truth can deny this fact. Nevertheless, there are people who find this very plain fact of embryology very little to their liking, and who therefore frequently attempt to brand it as a "falsification." But every university text-book in the hands of every student of medicine, which is used as a basis for the state examinations, contains a statement of this simple fact, and if any student were to deny it during his examination he would be severely reprimanded by the state examiner. People who still refer to such undeniable and scientifically recognized facts as falsifications place themselves outside the pale of all moral premises and scientific research.

It is a fact, then, that man is likewise descended from the fish.

But, if we ask how it happened and what were the external causes which transformed in the far off primitive days a fish breathing through gills into a land animal breathing through lungs, there is once more a living form which gives a direct clue. In a few small rivers of the eastern part of the Australian continent, a creature has been found which externally, so far as scales, fins and gills are concerned, resembles a large salmon or carp. But if we study its internal structure we find that it has also perfectly developed, serviceable lungs, and if we study its mode of living the logical purpose of this double supply of breathing organs becomes plain. During the dry season the little rivers of this region dry out almost completely. Nothing remains of them but a few pools of bad, brackish water in which the fishes are crowded together and encroach on one another's supply of air. Under these trying conditions, this strange animal swims to the surface of the water, draws air into its lungs and thus breathes after the manner of a genuine land animal, which dispenses altogether with water for breathing purposes.

This paradoxical fellow who can change himself at will into a fish and into a newt, has been called the "newt-fish," and its Latin name is Ceratodus. But this name was originally invented for the purpose of applying it to a band of fishlike creatures, which may be traced by fossil remains throughout a long evolution far back into the earliest Primary period, and which are distinguished by very peculiar teeth in the roof of the mouth. And the Australian Ceratodus of our day has exactly the same kind of teeth. Hence,

CERATODUS FORSTERI,

living in Queensland, Australia. It has gills, the regular breathing apparatus of fishes, but also lungs, the breathing organ of adult newts, frogs, reptiles, birds, and mammals.

we logically conclude that it has preserved this peculiar double method of breathing from the days of primitive creation, and we refer to it as a last straggler of a real transition group from primeval fish breathing through gills to the first primeval animal breathing through lungs—in other words, to that theoretical mixed group containing the principal characteristics of amphibians, reptiles and mammals. The fossil remains of those primitive relatives of Ceratodus are considered as parts of creatures belonging to this transition group. At all events, this Australian Ceratodus shows very clearly what the conditions are in which a lung may develop. This is simply the outcome of lack of water, or lack of air in the water.

Some might ask how it happened that a new organ could develop just when it was needed most, very much like a fairy table which is set whenever the wish is expressed. The witchery of nature can never come out of the unknown; it has always some logical connection. Indeed, the lungs of Ceratodus on closer study reveal the fact that they are merely a transformation of an organ which all genuine fish carry with them—the so-called swimming bladder. This swimming bladder forms a sort of balloon filled with air in the body of the fish, and it serves in the first place as a means of overcoming the weight of the fish in the water. This organ fulfills a useful purpose in rising and sinking, and to this end it was provided with a valve for its regulation. Many fish therefore retained an open connection between the swimming bladder, the intestines and the mouth for the purpose of inhaling or exhaling air. This is the starting point of the lungs. The balloon or bladder in the vicinity of the aesophagus being filled or closed at will, it served at the same time to feed the arteries of its walls with

A SHARK.
The sharks are a primeval group of ancestors of fishes and are related to the family tree of man.

oxygen. Once it had come into operation, it could under severe conditions be used as a substitute for the gills in times when water was scarce. When these conditions continued for a long period of time, the swimming bladder assumed this role permanently and became a genuine lung, while the gills atrophied until nothing remained of them but traces in the embryo. Thus the land animal sprang into being, or to express it with a view to the great line of our evolution man emancipated himself from the stage of water animals.

Now that we have found that Ceratodus is the living representative of another "bridge," or at least one side of it, we are naturally anxious to find the other pillar of that bridge. That is to say, we should like to know what other species of fish helped to make this bridge, for there is a wide difference between fish and fish.

When we mention fish to a layman, his first thought is of those kinds which he finds on his table and with which, under the present conditions of natural education, he is more familiar than with zoological literature. The overwhelming majority of table fish consists of so-called "bony fish," that is to say, all of them have a more or less solid skeleton. All of the European river fish belong to this class, the trout, the pike, the carp, etc., and such sea fish as flounder, herring and codfish. If we find a jar of delicious caviar on our table, or if our meal is crowned with expensive Russian sterlet, we meet another group of fish, the so-called Ganoids. The proudest representative of this class is the sturgeon, the eggs of which are used as caviar. These Ganoids are especially distinguished by the fact that some of them have a very soft skeleton, consisting of cartilage instead of bones.

This cartilage skeleton becomes permanent in a third group, which is not admitted to our table, but may be found on that of the Chinese, the sharks, which are known at least by name to everybody.

Separated from these three groups of fish by a wide chasm, there is a fish-like creature which is very highly appreciated by gourmands—the lamprey.

Finally, there remains one solitary and very strange little fish, the so-called lancet-fish or Amphioxus, which is distinguished from all other fish by the extreme simplicity of its structure.

A comparison of these five groups of fishes leads to the following conclusions in regard to the descent of man:

If it is a fact that Ceratodus is actually a part of that bridge which connects with man, then the other end of that bridge could not be found among fish with a bony and solid skeleton, but among those which have a cartilaginous skeleton, the foremost of which are the sturgeons. Ceratodus itself still has a soft skeleton similar to that of the sturgeons. It is true that amphibians, reptiles and mammals have a very solid skeleton,

more solid even than that of the trout and herring. It is evidently a separate adaptation. The
connecting link following the Ceratodus class is
found below the entire class of bony fish which
are once again a special side line.

The Ceratodus class of fish have still other
conspicuous relations to fish of the sturgeon class.

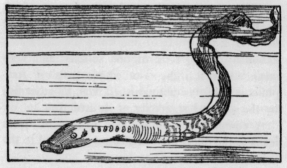

A LAMPREY,

the representative of a group of fish intermediate between the
Amphioxus type and the *Sharks.*

The historical evidence coincides with these
marks, for sturgeons were present in extraordi-
narily large numbers during the Primary age.
In fact, there were so many species of them that
they represented for a while the entire fish family
on this earth. Wherever we see in museums

their beautiful resplendent scales, there we are face to face with another disguise of man, which takes us far back to the very beginning of the Primary age.

Taking the soft skeleton as a basis for further research, it becomes evident that sharks are the next stage in our line of descent. The sharks played likewise a very prominent role in those primitive days, and to this day they are the most dangerous as well as the most intelligent of all fish. In a multitude of fine traits the shark is a genuine prototype of higher vertebrates translated into fish life. The simple plan of four limbs is sharply outlined in its fins, that characteristic which has become so full of meaning in the subsequent evolution. Our teeth, which have become so typical in their present form as a mark distinguishing man from all other animals, may be derived by strict anatomical logic from a basic plan found among sharks, which is actually startling for the layman. The shark has a formidable set of teeth. But, in its mouth, it has also developed a special trait in the way of thorny bristles which also appear in a less developed form in other parts of its body. The entire surface of the shark's skin is covered with peculiar and very fine, but rough, prickles, and the skin of the mouth has developed these into specially strong and solid thorns, evidently for the good purpose of holding on to the food of these fish. This is a typical illustration of the genesis of "teeth" and without this clue it would be a very difficult problem to explain their origin.

There are still further points of evidence. We have just seen that the shark has the basic plan of four limbs in the form of fins. The lamprey, on the other hand, has none of that as yet, but it has the beginning of a skull in a sort of skin and cartilage pouch. Amphioxus, finally, has not even a trace of that. This would give us another chain of evidence. The line of evolution seems to go upwards from Amphioxus by way of the lamprey to the shark, and other things which we observe at the same time fit very well into this outline.

Throughout this region in the process of evolution we find a number of details which do not become intelligible until we meet them again in very perfect forms in far higher stages. In the life processes of some sharks, for instance, a genuine placenta formation will suddenly appear, the embryo being nourished through a placenta. Like a flash of lightning the thought strikes us that nature at this stage suddenly tried something which was temporarily feasible and served as a means of adaptation, but was soon dropped, and did not reappear and become typical until the mammals arose.

Again, in the development of the eggs of the lamprey, we see a sudden flaring up of almost the identical method which has later become typical for the amphibians of the present day. All these things indicate that at this stage we meet once more one of those ancient mixed groups, typical for our line of descent, which contained the historical germs of all higher forms and were, so to say, reservoirs for all the possibilities of subsequent evolution.

At the same time, we approach at this stage an entirely new and exceedingly significant point of departure, the source of all vertebrates in general.

What is the characteristic mark of a vertebrate, including man? The back bone, that great internal prop of the body. Well, then, we see the back bone growing softer and softer among the Ceratodus class, sturgeons and sharks, and it seems to dissolve more and more the further back we trace it. In the lamprey and finally in Amphioxus this backward formation is almost completed. There the proud column has become quite a thin thread of cartilage. It looks as if the backbone had gradually melted away like a piece of sugar in coffee. The spinal cord is no longer surrounded by solid bone, it extends through the body as a string of nerves, just as it does among worms or insects. And nothing indicates that typical characteristic which divides vertebrates absolutely from all other animals, but the position of this nerve string above the cartilaginous thread and above the digestive tract, while in all other animals the great nerve string is always located below the digestive tract. The backbone is here called merely the "chorda," and we are here evidently at the point where the vertebrates dissolve into invertebrates.

And what does it matter? If man is disguised in a lamprey or an Amphioxus, then we may as well look for him entirely outside of the vertebrates. One species of lamprey, which bore their way into the bodies of other fish and live as parasites upon them, were still mistaken for worms by Linnaeus himself. And the discoverer of Amphioxus thought that he had found a snail, which it indeed resembles far more than a fish when we dig it up from its hiding place in wet sand and see its transparent and lancet-like little body.

Any way, it makes no difference theoretically,

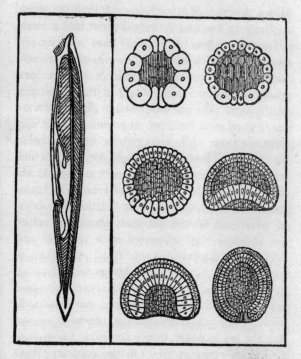

AMPHIOXUS LANCEOLATUS,

and its development in the egg. This development shows cross-sections, first of a hollow ball, then of the stage when this ball begins to double up, until an almost closed body with skin and stomach membranes and one orifice is formed. The last stage represents the so-called *Gastrula.*

if we descend still further even into the world of the very low and entirely invertebrate animals. Of course, in practice we shall have to apply, still more than heretofore, what we have previously said about circumstantial evidence. In the first place, one source fails entirely at this point, that of geology. We are compelled to push backward far beyond even the Primary period into the very dimmest time. All direct proofs suddenly fail at this stage. There are no fossils beyond the Primary ones. The minerals of more ancient epochs of the earth's development have been so transformed by a process of crystallization, the cause of which we do not yet understand, but which are in some way connected with pressure and heat, that impressions of fossil specimens of former living bones can no longer be discovered in them. Now these so-called crystalline slates are evidently the product of water, hardened sediments of the sea, and there is no reason to assume that the sea in which they were formed contained no living beings at all. On the contrary, there are important reasons contradicting such an assumption. The animals of the Primary period are far too highly developed to represent the very first animals on this globe, unless we renounce the idea of development entirely and believe that the first fauna and flora fell ready made from heaven. But the fact remains that from this time on we no longer find any remains of the ancient animals and plants. If we wish to make further conclusions we can only rely on the now surviving lower and lowest creatures and look for points of contact with them in the embryonic stages of higher animals.

With this understanding, we now proceed to discuss the further evidences on which we may rely from now on.

Among all the animals now known and living below Amphioxus, there is only one single small group which still shows a direct indication of a backbone, the so-called ascidians. These are small marine animals which are surrounded by a cloak of wood-like substance, very much as snails surround themselves with a well-nigh closed house. To judge by their general construction, these ascidians would be most logically classed among the worms, save for a few points of contact with mollusks. Among these ascidians a fine thread of cartilage appears, which has about the same position as the "chorda" of Amphioxus. Most of them have this cartilage only in the embryonic or larval stage, but a few of them preserve it for life. There is a strong possibility that the ascidians are very closely related to the vertebrates. It is true that on the one side they are buried deeply in the worm type far below Amphioxus. But on the other side they have the chorda, the first trace of a genuine backbone. But since some of them show this chorda only in the embryo stage, it seems evident that their ancestors had a still stronger hold on this rudiment, and were therefore still closer to the vertebrates than most of the present ascidians, which have evidently somewhat degenerated in this respect. So that Amphioxus and ascidians would be two branches of the common archetype which would, first of all, have developed the chorda. This archetype in order to produce the present-day ascidians must have been in all other respects unmistakably a wormlike animal. In short, we must look for other traces of man—in worms.

The term "worm" applies in the system to an enormous mass of different animals. There are hundreds of groups of fundamentally different worms. Some of them are of a higher order, with blood and sense organs and a genuine central nerve system. We would have to derive vertebrates most likely from them. If so, we should imagine a worm, which would not possess a chorda like Amphioxus or the lamprey, but would at least have a nerve string, which could later on develop into the spinal cord of a fish, and below which the digestive tract would extend in the form of a hose with one opening at each end of the body. The entire form would have no fin-legs, but would be a typical worm. This is the outline to which most of the present higher worms actually correspond.

At the same time we now find lower groups of worms which evidently belong further back in the scale. They have no complex nerve apparatus, no blood system and no opening at the lower end of the body. We are justified in assuming that they represent an older type, a sub-stage of the worm type. In other words, within the worm family we should have to look for man in various disguises leading from the complex to the simple. There is still something else to consider. In our system, apart from the vertebrates, there are still three other great groups of invertebrates which are of a higher organization than the worms. They are, first, the crustaceans, spiders and insects; then, the mollusks, such as snails, muscles and octopus and finally the echinoderms, such as star-fish, sea-urchins and related forms. Not even the most daring anatomical speculation can accomplish the miracle of deriving any one of these three classes from the other, and it is still less feasible to fit the vertebrates into any one of them. It would be impossible to develop an Amphioxus from a star-fish or an octopus. Some have attempted a theoretical line of descent from crustaceans to fish, but only by means of such a yawning chasm that no rational investigator went with them. The difference between these things is too great.

On the other hand, it is remarkable that all those groups may easily be traced back, each by itself, to some higher worm. It is true that the worm type to which the line of crustaceans and insects attaches itself and to which, for instance, our leeches and earth worms belong, is very different from an ascidian. Evidently there has been a great deal of individual evolution within the higher worm type. But nevertheless this picture presents a great deal of probability. The higher type of worm branched out into insects, mollusks, echinoderms and vertebrates, and it had four possibilities of evolution, among which only the vertebrate was destined to win the crown— the form of man. But this entire stage of worm life proceeded from some still lower worm which would therefore represent the next common station of all worms, and with them all men.

If we now try to get a conception of the worm in its lowest stage, we will find that its structure is wonderfully simple. Imagine for a moment that one limb after the other, one organ after another, is cut away from a man, arms and legs, the head, the spinal cord, the blood system, all the parts and organs between the stomach and skin, and that nothing remains finally but this skin and a stomach fitting it closely. Furthermore, let the rectum be closed, which gave to the higher organized worm the form of a hose, and only one opening remains for both assimilation and excretion.

Now such animals actually exist on the lowest plane of worm life. In certain jelly-fish, there lives a little parasite named Pemmatodiscus, which is literally composed of nothing but skin and digestive tract. There is also another animal in our fresh waters which is a little above this stage, the so-called Hydra. In the case of the Hydra, its lower end has grown fast to the soil, while its mouth is surrounded by fine tentacles, and a few other details are slightly better developed. Might it be possible that we could follow man down to this stage?

We sometimes speak of a man who consists only of "skin and bones." Well, that would still be a vertebrate man. But now, we are asked to eliminate also the backbone. Man is to consist only of skin and stomach. These two organs are now supposed to contain the germs of everything which is later on developed to full bloom in the human body, such as the nerve system, the blood system, the nutritive system, the sexual system, etc. This idea has seemed rather daring to some people, in spite of the fact that a mere consideration of the zoological system suggests it. There we finally likewise arrive at the Hydra by going from complex to ever simpler forms. There is no escape from this logic, if we venture at all into this vague domain of circumstantial evidence. If we do this, the logical line of research is the one we have followed. But there is still another one, and it is peculiar that it leads to exactly the same result.

We have not mentioned the embryo for some time, but now we shall ask it once more to act as a witness.

It is an anatomical possibility which, like all such extreme speculations, is mainly proven by its plausibility that another group of genuine invertebrates may be derived from such skin-and-stomach creatures as the Hydra, without passing through that other line of development in the evolution of worms. I speak of sponges, higher polypi and jelly-fish. These would form a definite circle, and all higher forms above the skin-and-stomach animals of the lowest class would be traceable to one common origin, viz., this skin-and-stomach animal itself. But now we recall that law which so frequently reproduces the portrait of ancestors in the formation of the embryo. If the circumstantial evidence is to be conclusive, then the embryonic development of all animals from the jelly-fish to the vertebrate ought to reproduce such a portrait, representing the double cylinder of skin and stomach with one single orifice, a prototype of Pemmatodiscus, or Hydra. Here again all resistance is useless. It is undeniable that such embryonic marks reappear in all nooks and corners of the higher classes of animals. It is that stage which Haeckel has designated as Gastrula.

It is hardly possible to find anything more different than a coral, a higher worm, a sea-urchin, a lobster, or a snail in the adult stage. Nevertheless, all of them show such characteristic skin-and-stomach larvae. They occur in many of the animals named and become more frequent with our progress in the direction of the lower formation, where we find them in the shape of a mere cylindrical embryo consisting of skin, stomach and orifice, and swimming about freely. In other cases, matters are not quite so plain, and we meet with all conceivable variations. But we have already seen that the biogenetic law never excludes such modifications. The essential thing is that even in the most daring deviations, the relation to the Gastrula form is plainly perceptible. In cases where no genuine cylinder is formed, we meet at least two layers in the cell, which are intended for the building of the body, one of them corresponding to the intestinal membrane of the genuine Gastrula, the other to the external skin.

Nor do these things end among vertebrates. On the contrary, the ascidians as well as Amphioxus still develop a typical Gastrula, a freely swimming "arch-tadpole," consisting of skin, stomach and orifice. And these relations remain plainly perceptible throughout the entire course of things, even in the embryonic life of the higher and highest vertebrates up to a man and including him. We speak of the Gastrula stage also among mammals, even if the external aspect of things no longer very closely resembles the original picture, but requires more careful investigation to complete the proof.

THE EVOLUTION OF MAN

It is now thirty years since Haeckel first conceived the idea that this continuous and persistent recurrence of the Gastrula embryo among higher animals has the simple meaning that all animals from the jelly-fish to man are descended from a certain archetype far down to the lowest root of the genealogical tree, which through all its life was nothing more than such a Gastrula. How this idea was derided and slandered in the beginning! But gradually one zoologist after another began to see that this idea of a Gastrula offered an excellent means of practical research in the process of evolution. Finally Haeckel's idea penetrated everywhere, and to-day this term, and the thing it stands for, are matters of fact in all embryological descriptions. In every text-book we read of the Gastrula. Especially the Gastrula formation of mammals has given rise to an entire literature, and writers are quite at home in their use of the term "gastrulation" in speaking of monkeys and man.

Under these circumstances, the further acceptance of Haeckel's logical conclusions is merely a question of our attitude toward natural evolution in general. If we accept it as probable to its remotest bounds, then we have no better and clearer sketch than this: In the early dawn of animal life, there lived creatures of a simple structure, such as that of the present-day Gastrula-larvae, or that of Pemmatodiscus, which are swimming about freely and represent creatures that persist all their lives in this stage. We may agree with Haeckel in thinking that these most ancient skin-and-stomach animals, for which Haeckel has proposed the general term of "Gastraea," at a very early stage tried two avenues of development. Some attached themselves with the closed end of their cylinders to the bottom of the sea and thus developed into a Hydra form. In the further development of this type followed a swarm of other sea animals, the so-called plant and flower types, such as sponges, corals, etc. But another group of the Gastrula forms adopted the creeping mode of life. Their bodies gradually approached the form of a symmetrical cylinder. This would be the line leading to genuine worms and then through vertebrates to man. At any rate we have for the present no simpler logical conception of the road which we traveled, and logic is indispensable so long as we are dealing with circumstantial evidence.

And now only one more short chain of conclusions remains—the last glowing mountain top in the morning light of our line of vision, before the curtain of white mist is drawn across it.

Let us start at once from embryology, which
pointed in the right direction in our quest for the
preceding stage.

How is the Gastrula type formed? Let us suppose a typical case in which the Gastrula is still
swimming about as a genuine skin-and-stomach
larva, a little cylinder with an orifice at one end.
This little cylinder arises before our eyes by a
very simple process. Its starting point is the
fertilized egg. The Gastrula-larva is composed
of many little building stones or cells. An adult
animal may consist of many millions of cells.
But the genuine egg from which the development
of the embryo starts, generally, after fertilization,
consists of only one cell and never more than
one. Just as surely as every human being comes
from an egg which is attached to the ovarium
of the human female and which through contact
with the semen of a human male becomes fertilized, just so surely this same human being also
comes out of one single cell.

Now between this single egg cell and the multi-
cellular Gastrula stage, we always observe the
following process, which occurs with iron consistency: The egg splits up into two cells by a
process of fission, and two cells become four,
eight, etc., until there is finally a lump of many

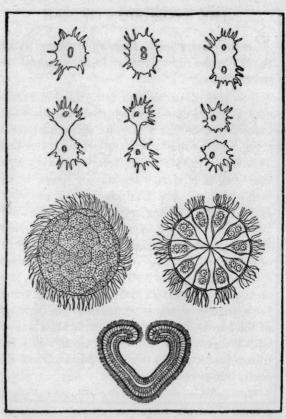

The figures on these two cuts represent the development of a uni-cellular arche-type and of a multi-cellular animal which preserved the simple form of a skin-and-stomach type. This is the idea of Haeckel as to the development of the simplest forms of animal life. To the right, we see the way in which a coral-animal, *Monoxenia Darwinii*, develops from the egg-cell. This cell divides into two cells, then into four, and finally, into a lump of cells. This lump develops fine bristles on its exterior surface, by means of which it revolves through the water. At the same time it forms a hollow in its center, then doubles up against itself, until it becomes a double-walled (skin-and-stomach)

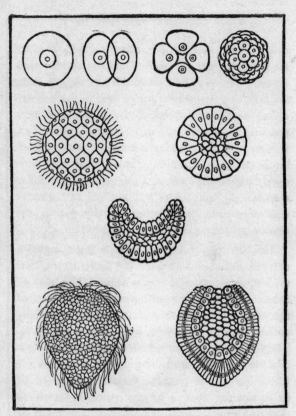

body, a *Gastrula*. The cuts on the left page represent the development of an *Amoeba*, a unicellular animal which remains so all its life, but propagates by fission. The two last cuts on the left page show an animal now living in the North Sea, *Magosphaera planula*. It never gets beyond this stage, which corresponds to the hollow ball stage of the corals. The last cut on the left page shows another animal now living, bisected. It is *Pemmatodiscus gastrulaceus*. Haeckel regards these living forms, *Amoeba Magosphaera*, and *Pemmatodiscus*, as present-day types of the primeval development of the animal world.

cells. In the center of this lump a hollow space is formed, and a closed hollow bladder thus arises. One part of this bladder gradually sinks inward, and its cells form a hollow, which becomes deeper and deeper, just as if a boy were pressing his finger into a perforated rubber ball. In this way the bladder becomes a cup, consisting of two cells bent against one another and wide open toward the center. The cells of the inner wall become stomach cells, and those of the outer wall skin cells, the opening of the gap is the mouth, and the Gastrula is complete.

This process, I repeat, is typical throughout, even in individuals, where the Gastrula itself is no longer the end of the process. The play of forces always begins with the disintegration of the egg cell into many cells, which gradually gather themselves into a lump like a mulberry. The tendency to form a hollow cylinder, or bladder, always exists and the final end is always the formation of the genuine Gastrula stage, or of its equivalent, that is to say, a double stratification of the cells by a primitive arrangement of the simple building material into two membranes.

If the biogenetic law has any meaning at all, it is that at this extreme end of evolution it has reached the climax of its consistency. The first throbs of the machine are still the same among all animals, man included. What can that mean?

Haeckel here made a significant suggestion. All animals from the lowest to the highest come out of one single cell. According to Haeckel, this indicates that the most primitive ancestor of all animals consisted all his lifetime of one single cell. It requires no great stretch of imagination to conceive such a uni-cellular animal. Even in our day thousands of animal species are living, every individual of which consists of one single cell. Why should not such creatures have lived at the time when all evolution began on the earth?

Among all classes of animals, the embryonic development begins with the fission of the one cell into many cells. This is exactly the way in which the present genuine uni-cellular creatures propagate themselves. Whenever one of these uni-cellular creatures is ready to propagate itself, it simply splits up into two, four or twenty pieces, as the case may be, and every one of these pieces in its turn becomes a new uni-cellular individual. Haeckel thinks that those primitive uni-cellular structures follow the same method, propagated in this way. But occasionally the offspring would cluster together and form the first larger clumps of cells. We know many uni-cellular animals that do this to-day. These clusters of to-day are mere aggregations of cells without any attempt at organization, and most likely the primitive uni-cellular clusters were likewise mere group aggregations. But gradually these cell aggregations of primitive times entered into more intimate social relations. They developed a certain division of labor. All this came about as a simple consequence of natural conditions.

All the cells in the cluster wanted to eat, each by itself, so all of them crowded outward when the cluster drifted about in the water. In consequence the cluster became a bubble, since all the cells arranged themselves on the surface and left the interior space vacant. This process at this stage is still very well illustrated by the early example of the Magosphaera. Under these conditions, the probability was nevertheless that all the rations obtained by the various cells would not be equal. The hollow bubble drifted through the water, or it gradually developed its own motion by the combined efforts of all cells, and thus it rolled against the tide. The cells on the upstream side then obtained most of the food, while the juices of the cells passed through the permeable walls of the individuals into the other cells clustered closely around them and down to the other pole of the bubble, so that all of them were fed. But nevertheless a certain part of this lump of cells gradually developed a capacity for special work in the interest of the entirety. The other cells did not remain inactive during this process. Since they were fed without being compelled to perform the work of actual eating, they devoted themselves much more actively to the movement and protection of the whole. The practical result was that the devouring cells were gradually surrounded by a wall of protecting cells, so that they assumed a sheltered position in the center and were literally under the shelter of the others. At the same time they had to remain in touch with the food that drifted down against them with the time. So they bent inward and formed a pocket by rolling themselves inside all the other cells, just like an inverted glove.

I am giving simply some general indications here, in order to suggest the way in which this development might have come about. Surely this, or some other method, must have been the cause of the cuplike form of uni-cellular animals, with the devouring cells, or stomach, in the center and the skin cells in the periphery, the prototype of the Gastraea.

But if this was true in the beginning of animal evolution in primitive days, it applies at the same time to man's evolution. It was also his first step: from a uni-cellular protozoon to the first multi-cellular skin-and-stomach animal, which stood still far below a sea-anemone, a jelly-fish, an earth-worm, or star-fish, but which contained the possibility of developing into anything, so to say, into an Amphioxus, a shark, a newt, a duck-bill, a primitive monkey, and, finally, into man.

Now, if man is contained in a uni-cellular protozoon, he stands at the same time at the very dawn of all known life. For not only animals, but also plants, may be derived from such living protozoa. To this day there exist such uni-cellular creatures which live by devouring other living creatures. We find others which feed directly on inorganic material, which eat, so to say, stones instead of meat and bread like the others. The one type contains the germ of the animal, the other that of the plant. The next logical thought will naturally be, that the representatives of the plant type were first in existence, and that the animal method developed as a secondary type, as a sort of parasitism at the expense of the other type. The vegetable organism consumed pure earth, and baked out of it, by the help of sunlight, its own "bread" or nourishing vegetable matter. The animal type developed by the gradual rise of the habit among some individuals of eating up their mates and thus assimilating "bread" in a prepared form. Evidently this must have happened at a very early stage among the protozoa. Later on the vegetable development went its own independent way. The animal continued to use the plant as a food, with occasional exceptions, where it devoured its own mates as a sort of third alternative. But both types later proceeded on their separate roads. The more intimate details of plant evolution do not concern us here. Suffice it to say that far down in the scale men are phylogenetically related also to plants, and to this day man still devours them.

There remains but one question. Man was contained in the germ in the very simplest forms of primitive life on earth. Wherever life goes, there he follows, down to the very atoms of existence. Is there perhaps a last possibility of deriving all life from "something else"?

I must discuss this question a little more in detail. It has always been a sort of parting of the ways for a great many people who thought about the origin of the human race, and in some unscientific circles this question is frequently played as a last trump for that very purpose. We may observe and note the fact that even the Darwinist mode of thought at this point permits of certain peculiar inconsistencies and differences among its champions. Men who are standing serenely on the ground with men as descended from animals have considerable disagreement at this last point of departure, and an unbiased discoverer cannot help coming to the conclusion that in matters of the origin of life itself no well established theory exists for the time being. So this point is constantly exploited as an open field. It is admitted that up to this point the arguments and facts are in favor of natural evolution. But henceforth everything is considered possible. The first life may have been "created"; in other words, it may have arisen without any adequate logical reason. Now this term "create" has something peculiar about it. If I as a human being "create" anything, there is always an adequate reason for it. Everybody knows that we cannot stamp armies out of the ground, or produce a field of corn by waving our hands. The smallest boy who whittles a wooden boat knows that he needs wood, knife, fingers and other things for that purpose. And as a matter of fact our entire practical life is permeated by this conception of cause and effect, of the inter-relation of the things which we must and will "create." If we apply merely this current conception of the term "create" to the evolution of man and of life itself, a little clear thinking will show that it coincides perfectly with the course of natural development of things from stage to stage. If we conceive of the fundamental forces of nature as something which can "create" things in the way that we do, thus creating finally man himself, we cannot admit from our own experience any other possibility for the creation of things than a simple and gradual procession leading step by step through the path of natural inter-relation. The most consistent form of Darwinism and this sort of creation do not exclude one another in any way; they rather coincide completely during the entire portion of the process. Evolution so conceived is merely a logical line of creation, and it is the immanent logical method of creation.

But the champions of the idea that the so-called first beginning of life is the end of Darwinism and the starting point of creation, do not apply these terms in the sense just explained. They are thinking of a creation for which we have not the least proof nor experience, and for which civilized mankind has no explanation except that of witchery, that is to say, an origin of things without any causal connection, without any premise, without adequate reason. Life is supposed to have arisen in its most primitive form by a miracle. There are a great number of people who fancy that they have rescued their entire world-philosophy by asserting a miracle at this one point. But most of them are of the opinion that they cannot accept the idea of evolution, and the animal descent of man from a protozoon, unless we admit a second miracle further up in the scale. Just as the first life cell at the lowest end of evolution is supposed to have been a miracle without cause, so the first genuine rise of consciousness, far at the top, in the first genuine human being, is explained by a miracle, regardless of any logical connection with the process of evolution. However, this last speculation is actually superfluous, even from the standpoint of those who champion it.

In my opinion, the fundamental facts of consciousness are found in every simple sensation. I feel this or that impression, light or dark, pleasure or pain; that, it seems to me, is the simplest form of "becoming conscious of anything," and this simplest form of sensation was doubtless possessed by the most primitive living cell. We may observe it in the very lowest forms of life. Moreover, modern scientific research cannot dispense with it as an inseparable quality of everything to which we apply the term "life." Of course, a uni-cellular protozoon, a radiolarian or an amoeba, does not reflect any stimuli in the same way that the infinitely more perfected and sensitive thought apparatus of human consciousness does. But these first animals nevertheless have the basic element of this reaction in their simplest sensation, such as avoiding light or twitching at a touch. Such an animal feels itself directly as an "I," if not consciously reflecting, then at least intuitively. The differentiation of sensations throughout the scale up to man is merely a question of an infinite chain of development without any interruption. But if it be assumed that the life of a protozoon, or an amoeba, was created by a miracle, then this same miracle simultaneously created consciousness, and all the rest could be left to the operation of the laws of transformism.

The question is only whether we must admit such a miracle even at this very first point of departure, were it only as a logical help, as a hypothesis even acceptable to the inductive method of scientific Darwinism and natural history. So far as I am personally concerned, I wish to emphasize that I have endeavored most earnestly for many years to arrive at an unbiased opinion on this question. I have asked myself again and again whether it could not be possible to meet our antagonists half way at this point, and thus do away with an unspeakably painful strife which is disturbing the work of civilization at the present time, and at the same time to reconcile two parties which have, each of them, a great number of worthy and absolutely honest representatives, who long for an understanding of the riddles of life. I am compelled to admit frankly that the result of all my deliberations has inevitably led to the same inexorable conclusion. The answer was always a determined "No." And it cannot be otherwise. Whoever is convinced of the causal and natural evolution of man from uni-cellular protozoa, cannot reconcile his logic with a change of method in explaining the existence of these primitive protozoa. He cannot at this point drop the principle of causal inter-relation on the chance of exchanging it for the principle of miracles.

Our logical thought, which is itself based on the principle of cause and effect, would have to demand in that case the same miracle for its own method of thought; it would have to do so to-day in myself and in every other student of nature. But this miracle never appears to-day, and so it must have been at the very beginning of things. The miracle failed to materialize then as it does now.

The situation is by no means so hopeless as the champions of miracles frequently represent it. All attempts at other logical explanations do not fail by any means at this point. There are quite a number of probabilities, none of them in any way miraculous, which we might discuss before we come to the question of the origin of the primitive protozoa. These possibilities may contradict one another and exclude one another, but they are nevertheless there, and most of them furnish a fairly firm support which we cannot pass by in silence.

It has been said that historical life certainly did not put in its first appearance on the earth at the point where to-day the most ancient fossil remains are found. It must have existed millions of years before that time, in order to arrive at the stage of development which meets us in these first fossils. Now there is nothing to prevent us from extending the term of evolution infinitely,— so far into the past that we arrive at a concept which human beings are in the habit of calling "eternity." The earth, which was present in that eternity, could very well have harbored from time immemorial the lowest forms of life, for instance, uni-cellular amoebae or bacilli or the earliest plant cells.

These primitive types reflect the result of some special stimuli which were due to the development of that time, and these types were then started into a course of higher evolution leading up to man. This theory is logical and perfectly sound. The living arch-cell in that case is simply an eternal form on this globe, and we may use these terms in the same way in which every student of physics speaks of heat as an eternal form of universal force.

However, this idea is combated by an argument taken purely from a universally accepted conception of geologists as to certain primitive historical evidence in the formation of the entire earth. There are certain valid reasons which speak in favor of the probability that this globe was an enormously hot and glowing body, such as the sun is even now, and contained all of its substances in a state of white heat or gas. Many of the reasons on which this conception is based have been found to be open to attack. But most of them still persist and are regarded as sound, and we have to-day only a very small number of genuine experts in geology who do not accept the theory of a sunlike stage of the earth.

This conception changes our picture of life processes. Life may be extended many millions of years beyond the time of the most primitive fossils. But finally there comes a time where the earth is a glowing ball of the temperaure of the sun, which transforms all metals into a hot gas and in which no amoeba can live or has ever lived. There are plants which live in hot springs and can stand a temperature of 100 degrees C., and dry spores or bacilli can endure a still higher temperature without perishing. But it is an absolutely impossible idea that an amoeba could still live in a world where even water cannot exist and where the heat keeps all elements permanently in a gaseous state, even iron. It is not until the globe has cooled sufficiently in ice-cold space to acquire a solid crust that the first precipitations of water with living beings of the simplest form are visible upon it. But even this state of affairs does not in any way justify the assumption of a miracle. There are two other possibilities which may be explained out of natural and logical conditions of existence on that globe.

THE EVOLUTION OF MAN

Some might ask at this point whether the most primitive and simple forms of life may not have immigrated and settled on the cooled globe. We know that small and large parts of matter are continually falling out of space upon the earth, the so-called meteorites. Might not the germs of life fall likewise upon our planet in the same way? The simplest spores of bacilli, such as are perpetually whirling through the air, would have been sufficient to carry the germs of life for all stages of evolution up to man on the surface of the globe. The spores of such bacilli endure a cold temperature of more than 200 degrees C. The temperature of space will certainly not be much lower than that, and the bacilli of this kind also can get along for a long time without any air, so that the space without any air between the different planets and suns would not be an obstacle to the transmission of living spores of bacilli. It is not at all necessary to fall back on the assumption that a meteorite, which by the way is generally ignited by the friction of the earth's atmosphere, must have carried the germs of life. The earth's atmosphere may have been "infected" directly by floating germs. Such a conception leads finally to the idea of "eternity" of the lowest forms of life. It would be very easy to imagine that certain spores of the simplest living matter are distributed throughout space from all "eternity," the same as the dust of iron and other elementary substances. These germs, held in a sleeping state so long as they are drifting in the cold atmosphere far away from air and water, would wake to genuine life and develop to a higher form as soon as a sufficiently cooled world body should offer them air and water. But who is going to determine by means of our limited instruments and the present imperfect state of our knowledge of bacilli, the origin of every one of the myriad spores which are floating round us everywhere? However, we are not at all compelled to accept this one hypothesis in order to rescue our idea of causality. There is a second and better explanation which has always had some champions, but would have had still many more if it had always been put in such a form as is required in order to meet all crude objections.

It has been said that life developed at a certain period, when the conditions for its rise existed, and developed out of the so-called inorganic dead matter in the same way in which a certain chemical combination, say water out of oxygen and hydrogen, or crystals, arise under given conditions. This conception stated in this bare form is startlingly simple. There were enough inorganic substances on this planet, even though in a state of white heat. Whenever a planet cooled, all these substances passed through certain stages of development. Water, for instance, then became an inevitable product of evolution. Why should not life be another product, like water, which developed also at that stage from so-called dead matter? Many very clear and circumspect brains have been satisfied with this simple formulation of the theory of life, and welcomed it as a perfectly rational solution. While in our present historical period life comes only from life so far as we know, it was assumed that in those primitive days the first life rose out of inorganic matter, and this was called "spontaneous generation." And it was generally considered an open question whether such "spontaneous generation" took place only in the beginning, or whether it may have taken place in subsequent ages, occasionally even to-day, along with the normal mode of generation, at least among the very lowest animated beings, though it has never been observed. Now it cannot be denied that this mode of solving the riddle is neither a serious nor a convincing one. It is indeed simple, but so is the solution of the Gordian knot which, according to the legend, was not solved by a clear grasp of the question, but by a blow of the sword. The idea of evolution requires that the thing which develops must explain the cause of its development by another thing out of which it developed. There must be as close a relation between these two things as there is between father and son, a deep-seated and intimate likeness combined with an assumption of differentiation through progress. Such a relationship and likeness exist between certain chemical and physical qualities and parts of the living amoeba, and such simple chemical combinations of so-called inorganic substances, as water, air and the like. But there is no such likeness in regard to the most characteristic mark of an amoeba, that is to say, subjective feeling, which is completely missing in purely chemical reactions. Here, we have the old and always reliable philosophical axiom that "sensation" cannot be derived from mere "motion." It is true that the field of sensation likewise is strictly under the control of the law of causation and does not admit of any "miracles." But, for this very reason it is never possible to derive a process of sensation from so totally different a thing as a process of motion in physics and chemistry. In the chain of cause and effect, feeling is only followed by feeling and motion by motion. The place of a link in one series is never taken by a member of the other series. The attempt to substantiate this statement in detail would lead too far away from our subject. Suffice it to indicate that the distinction between feeling and motion must be a fundamental demand of every refined and workable theory of understanding. And an ignoring of this demand would carry us into a fatal labyrinth of ideas. It may seem at the first glance that this statement kills the idea of "spontaneous generation" with one blow. But this is by no means the case.

It hits merely the crude conception of it. In order to give it a more refined and impregnable form, it is necessary to extend somewhat our definition of the "inorganic," that is to say, of nature below the first living cell. We may then maintain our hypothesis that the first cell, the first genuine living being, arose on this earth through natural development, when the surface of the globe had cooled to a certain temperature, and it originated out of the so-called inorganic substances of the earth which had long been present. We have only to add that these substances

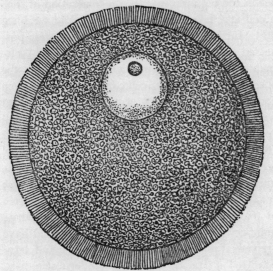

A HUMAN OVUM,

bisected and strongly magnified. Its actual size is that of a dot barely visible to the naked eye. This ovum, when detached from the female ovarium, represents a genuine "cell." It is surrounded by a membrane, which is penetrated by the male sperm-cell in the act of fertilization. The soft interior mass contains a large "nucleus."

had not formed any genuine living cell up to that
time, but they nevertheless possessed in themselves the requirements for the generation of such
a cell at a favorable temperature. And we must
add, furthermore, that these substances possessed not only the chemical and physical elements of matter and motion out of which the
special structure of the cell could rise under given
conditions, they also had a general basic element
of feeling out of which the same life of the cell
could be built. In other words, we must start
from the simple assumption that, in some way,
feeling is a basic property of all matter in the
universe, including all inorganic substances. This
fundamental quality is not affected by any degree
of temperature, nor dependent upon it. A large
number of the clearest thinkers in this field have
arrived at this idea by various roads and have
admitted it frankly. Among modern scientists,
I mention only Fechner and Haeckel.

Haeckel, who has championed and popularized
this idea of "spontaneous generation" more ener-
getically than any other man, has at the same
time incessantly emphasized in various parts of
his works that he considers primitive feeling as
an essential and fundamental quality of all matter
in the universe. If this is understood, we shall

have no further difficulty in accepting the idea of the natural evolution of life on the surface of this globe. In this case life would simply represent one point of aggregation, a focus of that one faculty of nature, "feeling." It would simply be a product of concentration, much as the formation of the entire sun or earth represents a product of concentration of another faculty, gravitation. This product of concentration may have had its own peculiar chain of causation. Considering that we have found life only in connection with definite chemical conditions which do not admit of any white heat, there is nothing to prevent us from assuming that its own laws of evolution could not arise until the primitive heat of the globe had been mitigated.

Let us also mention at this point that Fechner and more precisely Preyer, also considered the possibility that the cell life known to us might represent merely a product of adaptation to a cooler atmosphere, while the concentration of feeling in the primitive atmosphere of the sun was conditioned on another chemical form of adaptation useful in that other environment. But in principle all this is immaterial, and we apply the term "life" only to cell life between the stages of the amoeba and man. This life, at all events, did not arise until the earth had passed the stage of red heat. This would be the historical stage at which the conditions became favorable for the much discussed "spontaneous generation."

It was necessary to touch upon this rather difficult line of thought at least to this extent, because the confusion which reigns in this regard is very general and fatal. No one can be obliged at present to champion any one of all these theories. But one thing at least must be admitted, we are not in such need of ideas for a natural explanation of life that we are absolutely compelled to seek refuge in miracles. Of course, while we are still in the field of the "natural," we must also admit frankly on the other hand that our actual knowledge of the fundamental problems of life is still so incomplete at this day that it is well to pursue our studies along many different roads. It is quite probable that in our further research along this line, we shall meet many surprises and find many new theories, for we know very little of the internal processes that take place even in the simplest cell. There is still a world before us which we have barely touched. But not all riddles lie concealed on the side of life. We are also far from seeing clearly into inorganic problems, all declarations to the contrary notwithstanding. The simplest processes of crystalline formation, in which by some internal means definite individual forms are produced, are still as dark to us, so far as their causes and inter-relations are concerned, as the nature and origin of the living cell. The simple mechanical process of attraction and repulsion is still as unknown to us as the simple fundamental process of feeling. If we deliver man at the boundary of primitive life on earth into the hands of these mysteries, we are merely conscious of the fact that we have taken him back to the limits of our present perceptive powers. Beyond that limit we do not venture. We simply maintain that the law of causation is not interrupted at that boundary, and we agree with the astronomer, who does not doubt that the law of gravitation is still in force even in those places, which he cannot reach with his eyesight or his instruments.

There is still another thing which is intimately connected with the condition of our present knowledge concerning the origin of life. To understand quite logically at present all the laws of evolution of this life involves an understanding of the first problem. We have watched the disguises through many different forms of animals which man assumed in the course of his development. These animal forms become ever more imperfect, ever more simple, until they reach the uni-cellular protozoon. There is no doubt that we have watched the general course of a grand upward evolution, the highest and most central branch of which is topped by man himself. But now we should naturally like to know what was the compelling motive of this development. What controlled and determined the laws of growth and development? Why did not the first cell remain a primitive cell? Why did it not continue to generate nothing but primitive cells in all the millions of years? Why did some of its offspring rise higher and higher, up to the triumphant summit of mankind? These questions are certainly natural, and they are the object of a large part of that scientific research to which we apply the general term of Darwinism.

However, this is another problem. We may submit the course of evidence which I have outlined from man to amoeba and may still believe that we do not know anything definite about the compelling motive of this development. We may calmly say that we know too little of the origin and fundamental laws of life and cannot command at present an understanding of the laws controlling the development of life by studying them directly. We may be content to watch the finished work of those laws, the uninterrupted chain from amoeba to man.

If there is one who does not care to go so far with us, he will at least emphasize that all our theories of the nature of these laws must necessarily be loose, changeable and capable of improvement in view of the present state of our knowledge. It is true that this is frequently overlooked. We often hear it said that Darwinism is on the decline. It is claimed that Darwinism is dissolving and disintegrating into a wild confusion of different opinions among the experts, and that not a stone of the original building of the principle of Darwinism will remain in the near future. But this is sheer nonsense, so far as that line of facts is concerned, which we have presented in this work, that line which connects all living beings by one common descent and locates man himself on this genealogical tree. These facts are daily becoming more impregnable and firm, and we may calmly spread them among the people as a secure acquirement of scientific research. But it is true, and not at all a matter for surprise from the standpoint of the theory of evolution, that there is a great difference of opinion as to the nature of the active principle of development. The general mistake of confounding this special field of research with the whole of Darwinism may perhaps be pardonable when we remember that Darwin himself has speculated a great deal about these "laws," and whoever wishes to write on these things, to discuss them, either for or against Darwinism, and instruct others about them, should at least be sufficiently trained in scientific thought to distinguish between these two departments of science.

Darwin tried in his time to give us a clear formulation of the laws of evolution, by which he did not attempt to prove *that* all living beings developed out of one another, but *why* they did. If this formulation is true, it is a matter of course that it would also comprise man and show us why he had to develop.

Darwin's theory is based on the following line of thought. Here we have a simple, primitive animal form. It is so far adapted to external conditions and has developed such faculties that it can exist, maintain itself, and propagate its kind. But now a long space of time elapses. We then find in place of this animal form a new one, which is much better adapted to the same conditions. Or, again, these conditions have also changed in the meantime, and we observe to our surprise a new animal form, which is still in many points like the old one, but also adapted to the new conditions. What has happened? This sketch, according to Darwin, represents in principle the entire evolution. The conception of better "adaptation" includes also mental progress, brain evolution, and in this way a road leading from amoeba up to man produces the entire line of descent which we have been tracing. To explain this line of march would be equivalent to explaining the steps from an amoeba to a man. And Darwin attempts this explanation.

The first archetype propagated its kind. This offspring consisted of individuals which, for some reason or other, were not entirely alike. They were all individuals, differing more or less, just as the children of some parents differ among human beings, just as the offspring of plants differ, and just as a brood of rabbits have different colors. These variations represented either an advance or a retreat compared to the characters of the archetype. Some of the offspring were superior to their parents, others were average individuals, and still others were

inferior. Now these individuals entered **into** competition with one another for the means of life and into a struggle against the conditions surrounding them. In other words, they entered into the "struggle for existence." The result of this struggle was different for different individuals. The superior type, which were best adapted or adaptable to their environment, succeeded best in propagating their kind and in surviving in the greatest number, while the average type and those inferior to it succumbed. In this way, only the superior breed survived and propagated its kind. The offspring of this superior type were in their turn subjected to the struggle for existence. A selection of the fittest operated on them as it did on their predecessors. This continued uninterruptedly. In the course of the various generations, continuous improvement, an up-breeding of the type, and a more and more perfect adaptation as well as fitness to survive, naturally resulted. Furthermore, there was another possibility which must be considered. A change took place in the external conditions, suddenly requiring of the living beings an entirely new adaptation. In that case, it was not the superior type developing along the line of the improvement of the parent type which had the advantage, but certain individuals which departed most widely from the parent form in a certain direction corresponding most nearly to the new requirements. Take it, for instance, that the climate changed. A plain formerly covered with a brownish mould was suddenly and permanently covered with snow. The brown plain had been inhabited by brown rabbits. Up to the time of this sudden change it was always those individuals of the offspring which most closely resembled in color the tint of this plain that survived in the struggle for existence; for brown coincided with brown and was not easily detected by the enemies of the rabbits. But now white suddenly became the best adapted color. Henceforth those rabbits had the greatest chance to survive which happened to be white as a result of individual variation. These were now preserved, they propagated their kind and left behind them a growing number of young, which continued to marry white with white. In the course of years the entire rabbit nation became white—an adaptation to snow.

This logic of Darwin's seems irresistible so long as we admit that individual variations always offer sufficient material for selection—in other words, that there were always a sufficient number of individuals following by natural selection a line of development improving the archetype; and, furthermore, also a number of other individuals varying according to special adaptation.

Once this assumption is granted, all the rest is merely a mathematical problem, the mill of evolution being forced to grind. But the question of superior characters and individual variations contains many deeper problems, as Darwin himself was well aware. What was it that determined the number of superior individuals and special adaptations, what was the determining factor guaranteeing the presence of certain individual characters in every case?

This point has been the object of incessant discussion, and the end of it is not yet. We might believe that the life methods of the parents themselves might, in a certain way, have a determining effect on the appearance of certain characters among different people. For instance, if I am a passionate ball player all my life, is it possible that there may be at least one of my children which would have inherited a talent for ball playing? The explanation of the problem has been attempted. It was declared that exercise on the part of the parents would always serve to pave the way for inclinations of the children along the same line. The logical outcome of this argument is a position which had been aimed at long before Darwin by Lamarck. In the last analysis, the selection in the struggle for existence might be entirely eliminated so far as the pure intensification of hereditary tendencies is concerned, and all specially adapted children could be considered as the outcome of special characters acquired by the parents through special exercise. Apart from the fact that this explanation does not explain some other things and is not satisfactory to us in a good many other respects, for instance, when we are called upon to explain how exercise should be able to heighten or change the color of brown rabbits, there is one great difficulty which is not met by this theory. It has been denied that characters acquired by the parents through exercise could ever be transmitted to offspring. If I play ball for thirty years and all my muscles and nerves are perfectly trained for that purpose, and if at the end of that time I propagate my kind, it is supposed to be impossible that a child then born should be more predisposed in its bodily structure for ball playing than any other child. August Weisman carried this doubt to its extreme. It cannot be said that he has made his point. But his objections have at least demonstrated that even the simplest facts are at present very hard to present and explain. In another direction, Hugo de Vries has attempted to show that the formation of varieties, superior types and talents, is far more extensive than Darwin ever suspected, no matter what their cause may be. De Vries thinks that there is a great periodical process of formation which takes place side by side with the simple and minute variations of the offspring of any species, and this greater process develops an enormous number of new forms. This struggle for existence then selects from this large number those of less value for the time being and eliminates them, and the surviving species will appear as perfectly new ones. This idea, the so-called "Mutation Theory,' has not been sufficiently explained, although it is doubtless a very important suggestion.

The opinions of the scientists are still divided on such points as these, because there are evidently still many logical and natural possibilities which affect the obscure problem suggested by Darwin. It is quite certain that the problems of the means by which variations are brought about are of the highest importance for the descent of man. But these problems run parallel to the question of descent which we have discussed in this little volume, and it is not necessary to wait for an explanation of those ulterior questions, nor to substantiate the claims here set forth. In regard to all these researches, we meet at present a temporary limit to our perceptions and understanding, but this does not prevent us from enjoying the results of the studies which we have carried to success within the present field of acquired knowledge.

The question of the descent of man belongs to one of the fields which are thoroughly conquered by science, and neither complaints nor doubts can alter this fact. There is nothing more to do but to meet these things bravely. Human beings ever remain what they are. No one can rob them of their nature. All our ideals likewise remain undisturbed. Whoever feels within himself the force of a deep spiritual life, the living breath of nature, will not be wrecked by the fact that his ancestor did not only wear a rough and hairy animal skin as a protection for his naked shoulders, so and so many years ago, but also at a certain period previous to that wore an animal skin grown fast to his own body. Poetry did not die when it became known that it is not the sun which actually rises in the east, but the earth which revolves toward it. Genuine religious feeling is truly something very human, using these terms in their very widest and sublimest meaning, and a cold fact from the history of human evolution cannot dampen this spirit. It is a triumph of modern human powers that we can resurrect the past from the tombs of millions of years. That is what makes those ancient pictures so inspiring. But we should not be worthy of this triumph if we did not have the strength to dominate the spirits of the past with the calmness of a master who can look at them serenely and say: "You are of the past and the struggles of the past belong to you; but *I* am, and above me are *my* stars."

THE END